W9-DIF-170

Books by Richard Fariña

BEEN DOWN SO LONG IT LOOKS LIKE UP TO ME
LONG TIME COMING AND A LONG TIME GONE

Recordings by Richard and Mimi Fariña

CELEBRATION FOR A GRAY DAY
REFLECTIONS IN A CRYSTAL WIND
MEMORIES

LONG
TIME
COMING
AND A
LONG
TIME
GONE

Well, kings die easy when nobody cares
and queens have smiled on the gallows
and dukes have vanished while saying their prayers
and heirs have drowned in the shallows
    and the lords have laughed while falling in flames
    and ladies have died of dishonor
    and counts have exploded while sunning in Spain
    and knights have stewed in their armor

but the jack, jack o'diamonds,
jack o'diamonds is a hard card to play.

Now cowboys die in the arms of a friend
while the sun's conveniently setting
and Cherokees go to their feathery end
while everyone's home minuetting
    and generals fade very slowly away
    while golfing and drinking martinis
    and generals' girlfriends have dropped in the grave
    while wearing highheels and bikinis

but the jack, jack o'diamonds,
jack o'diamonds is a hard card to play.

Now presidents sink on schooners-of-state
and banks have failed from corruption
and congressmen perish at open debate
and lawyers have choked on deductions
    and rich men die from sugary food
    and paupers die when they're reeling
    and wise men go out in a hungover mood
    and virgins die once, without feeling

but the jack, jack o'diamonds,
jack o'diamonds is a hard card to play.

RICHARD FARIÑA, 1966

LONG TIME COMING AND A LONG TIME GONE

By <u>RICHARD FARIÑA</u>

Foreword by Joan Baez

Notes by Mimi Fariña

 RANDOM HOUSE / NEW YORK

Mimi Fariña's notes were transcribed from a tape recording of her conversation with Christopher Cerf, December 23, 1968.

This one is for **DICK'S MOTHER AND FATHER**

Foreword
CHILD
OF DARKNESS

I'll tell you what he was in my eyes. He was my sister Mimi's crazy husband, a mystical child of darkness—blatantly ambitious, lovable, impossible, charming, obnoxious, tirelessly active—a bright, talented, sheepish, tricky, curly-haired, man-child of darkness.

Remember that he was my brother-in-law—husband to one sister Mimi, close friend to the other sister, Pauline, and mystical brother to me. He'd won me full over by the end, from a hostile, critical in-law of Dick the intruder, to a fond friend. By the end we sisters and many other people had some of Dick's blood running in our veins, and mad Irish-Cuban thoughts in our heads.

Dick worried about the monkey-demon on the night of the full moon, and kept a little stash of pot in a cut-away hole in the center of an old book on the Irish Revolution. He carried in his wallet a tiny leather box from India which held a hair and a piece of paper with two words written on it in a strange language, and which mustn't be opened until just before its carrier was to die. He talked by candlelight

late late into the night with Mimi—all about the cards.
And then he cut the deck for himself and drew the King
of Hearts. Happy in the strange night, he made Mimi cut a
card for herself, and she drew the Queen of Hearts. And
they were close and certain and frightened and "Mimi," he
said, "you do one for Joanie. Come on, one for Joanie."
And Mimi cut me the Jack of Diamonds. And this too . . .
that out of all the angles and candles and king purple and
gold and burgundy red and hushed magnificence of the
ancient cathedral at Chartres, Dick spied a tiny black alcove, and as he whispered toward it he saw that it had in
it, among other miniature statues, strange little demon figures, the same demons he felt he knew by heart.

But Dick's thorny demons of the night hid themselves
during the day from the sun which shone on a fairyland of
beauty. A fairyland of thoughts and images of swallows
and rose petals and new love and the eternal blossoming
springtime of another land. In this other land he took his
friends by the hand, and strutted and bowed and doffed his
hat, and played a million roles, wrote a million songs and
a million poems, swished his dulcimer from under a tree
and sang and talked before a million people. Also in this
land he was a writer, which was not such grand fun all the
time, which was hard work and which no one seemed to
understand, and which tested Dick as a young man and
Mimi as his second wife.

I knew Dick then, in that odd world for those few years,
those typewriter-and-spaghetti years which got a little
plusher toward the end. And he and Mimi never went under. They never really thought about going under because
it was too much fun treading water. And besides, they liked
each other lots, and Dick and Mimi had a most extraordinary and rare capacity for having fun.

Out with Mimi, so proud, so proud, on a dress-up night.
A fancy French restaurant night—a candles, wine, suit and
cufflinks night. After the what shall I wear fuss—after the

shall we tie the dog or leave him in the house fuss—"Mimi, turn off the heat."

"No. Leave it on, it's freezing when we get home."

"I don't care. Do you want the house to burn down? Sometimes something falls right down in there and catches fire. I know, Mimi, I've smelled it." (He was afraid of ants, too, ants in the house because one would crawl into his ear while he slept and make him crazy, or kill him.) Bustle, bustle—the keys—lock the door—mumble—unlock the door—stomp—slam—out into the California evening. No, no, the Carmel evening. A raging sunset over the sea. Proud Dick, all handsome and healthy and young and English Leather—planning—planning—restaurant, reservations—calm beautiful Mimi three paces ahead to the car, calm, calm. Dick cocky, busy, planning—but then suddenly, suddenly the lost look of a child who had planned to please everyone at once and everyone equally—who by some imagined oversight is momentarily stopped in his tracks and confused and curiously hurt—Dick's startled face in the red sunset caught my eye—and Mimi, with the quick flash of compassion which you and I have had at least once, and which can for a second, or a minute, or for hours upon reflection, break your heart sorely, "Oh, Richie! Oh, Pumpking!" and there like grace with a laughing smile she hugged him and he sprang back to earth.

"I was just thinking," he said.

Sometimes they would tell me about the fancy dinners. Quite simple. When two people dress up and wear amethyst and toast each other by candlelight, they glow. And it makes everyone around swing a little.

A dinner at home. At Dick's house. Yes, I remember. Dick would cook with garlic. Tons of garlic. All other foods were secondary. There would be music. Loud music— Gospel, or Vivaldi, or the Beatles. I can remember a Beatles night. Dick was an automatic host, and that evening as friends began to wander in the door he waved his onion-cutting knife, turned the music up past the pain threshold and began salad-directing Mimi. Mimi made exasperation faces as she began to labor over the greens. The house was at a low rumble. No mustard. Over the Beatles everyone must understand no mustard. Dick would die in a flash from mustard allergy. Simply clog up somewhere in the pipes and smother to death. Someone poured the wine and more guests came and the house was heavy with spice smells. Small talk about Carmel and big talk about Vietnam. Carmel had been beautiful that day and Johnson was a monster and had terrible-looking ears. Also, shouted Dick, he prayed on Sundays and killed Orientals all week and that was pretty revolting by itself. Everyone agreed. One more round of wine and a record change and dinner was on. A last guest knocked and was admitted. He was new. A glass for the new guest. Bring him to the table. Hello, hi, hi, groovy, sit down. And that night the new guest said it by chance. There was always an opening line. The new guest, by chance, over the clapping and stomping of the Birmingham Back Home Gospel Choir, offered unwittingly, "It's been a splendid day . . ."

"Yes!" said Dick. "A splendid day. Splendid. Splendid day for grouse!"

And he raised his wine glass high to the roars of laughter. The new guest was initiated and blushing and on his own, and we teased Dick for his timing and began to eat. Dick held his fork European style and mashed bits of food onto it with his knife. I watched him heap it to overweight, raise it halfway to his mouth and then pause with great drama. One of the regulars to his right was gulping milk. He turned toward her.

"Agatha."

Agatha. It was her name for the evening and it was delivered in high English. "Must you drink your milk with such an incredible amount of onomatopoeia?"

The regular didn't know what onomatopoeia was but laughed anyway. Dick nodded to his wife and commenced eating. All right. If Dick would be high English, I would be low English. Not only would I be low English, I'd be blind and in a wheelchair. I was interrupted in the middle of my fantasies.

"Samantha." That was me. "I believe I heard you belch. I do prefer my own gastronomical fluids. We all do choose our savories to our own taste. Eat up, dear. Chew each bite succulently." I burped and was preparing a comment.

"Eloise, you're beginning to perspire. Would you like a Phillips tablet? Would you like the pukka boy? Shall I ring for Rob?"

The laughing was steady from that point on with pauses for eating and changes of character. Dick commanded and directed the show, swaying the tide of nonsense, starring but always tugging at the quiet ones to try out the fun—to laugh. Before a night was over he would have gone German officer, gone Festus Turd from Texas, gone Indian foreign-exchange student, gone paralyzed, gone weightless, gone blind, and gone mad. I would go with him because I loved it. It was crazy and it was fun, and the night roared by as we laughed ourselves teary-eyed.

That dinner ended with a salad fight, when a piece of sliced tomato knocked a Mexican plate off the wall from directly over my head. The house was rented and so was the plate, of course, so we felt dampened and all gave serious thought as to how to glue up fifty pieces of crumbly plaster. We gave up, had a plate funeral, talked about politics for a while, lingered, felt good, and finally went home.

I laughed to myself, reflected upon the evening and felt enormously grateful and happy. Those nights of fun, hosted by the Black Irish Mad Hatted Rose—those nights are what I miss most of all since Dick died.

Dick died before he ever figured out how he felt about "making it." What he meant when he said "making it" was the Hollywood thing—having money and fame and a public image. Dick and I knew when we talked how stupid the whole concept was—that a public image was based upon

some truths, some half-truths, some innocent rumors and a
few nasty lies. It meant general overexposure and self-
consciousness (as opposed to self-awareness) and the constant danger of accepting someone else's evaluation of you
in place of your own—your own being practically impossible to make already. Money meant power, an irresistible
prestige value, and lots of extra attention—all of which
could be used, almost in spite of themselves, for good things
if you kept your head. We also knew the meaning of the
word temptation, and what a smart thing it was for Jesus to
say, "Lead us not into temptation," because He knew well
that once we got there we were all so very weak.

Sometime, not too long before the carnival ended, Dick's
wild carousel slowed down long enough for him to write
these words in a song to Mimi—

> Now is the time for your loving, dear,
> And the time for your company.
> Now when the light of reason fails
> And fires burn on the sea,
> Now in this age of confusion
> I have need for your company.

JOAN BAEZ

Contents

LONG TIME COMING AND A LONG TIME GONE

Dick got the idea for this story, I'm pretty sure, after having seen or heard Martin Luther King— probably either on television or radio. In fact, we used to listen to that record of King's Washington speech ("I Have a Dream"); Dick may have started thinking of this story then. Other than that, I'm not really sure where this all came from, except his own paranoia.

Dick wrote the story in '64–'65 in a little cabin in the Carmel Highlands; I have a picture of him writing it. He was able to write no matter where he was—in a tiny cabin, or in a car, or on the beach.

"Long Time Coming . . . ," incidentally, is a line from an old blues—like "Been Down So Long It Looks Like Up to Me."

M.F.

Chicken fat. Black chicken fat, that's all he smell like. Three four mile away he come stepping off the bus, no matter what kinda grease he got up under his arms, no matter what kinda pomade, you smell him, whiff.

True enough I don't get that close 'cept the one time I give him the business. But down the Preparation and Readiness Club there's a couple that got it good. They're waiting at Trailways when he come off, Harlem-New York suit, little secret lapel pin, shined shoes, press reporters paying out attention like he was up for space in the legislature. The TV taking down words what he speak. Nicreamus his name, something like that, stole out of the Bible. Nicreamus Loam. Agent for the conspiracy.

The two boys from the club hang back, let pictures get took, count the crowd standing around, see who there and who ain't, take names, listen to the speech he make.

Sedition. Full of black sedition and propaganda. Anyone can tell. "Hundred years," come Murtagh Feud mocking, pinkies in his nostrils. Murtagh looks the part when he minds, head like a bull's only bigger, baby fat. He's local deputy, full time, acting chancellor of the Preparation and Readiness Club. He roll back his lips, bug his eyes, keeps going. "Hundred years the spade say. Emancipation, civil rights, using words like he ain't no nigga atall, regular Yankee voice like some announcer in the newsreel."

"He's passin'," come Billy-Dick Mangle, other boy who scouted the bus stop. "Pretty boy, he look just like Feud here." Murtagh scratching his head like a monkey, jump around and everybody laugh a little, ready for fun. But he stop when he getting our attention, and go so fast-serious you have to listen. "This Loam," he say, "is one nigga ain't passin' nohow let me tell you. He got certificates all right, even books his name's in. But that don't change that skin

none, that hair." Everybody murmur, nod their heads. "I
tell you how he's passin'. He go by you buck naked some
December night with no moon, you won't see him 'less he
smiles. That's how *he's* passin'."

"You smell him too," come Mangle, and the members
chuckle, everybody sitting around the war table the time
I'm telling about, making plans for the crisis. "You smell
that chicken-fat smell."

"Couldn't be much else," say Feud, pinkies up there
again. "All the grease they sopping in with hardtack.
Bound to emit some noxious fumes." Then we mix it up
again, laughing, talking about his bodily parts.

Now this thing happening round the basement where
the field marshal got his home. Everyone have some kinda
name in West Tennessee, that's how they get to join, me
the youngest, thirty-two next birthday, been a member one,
maybe one and a half years. The club come to emergency
session three four times since I join: first right after that
initial sit-in Birmingham tactic, then immediate after each
major crisis, whenever there's threats to what the field
marshall calls sovereign personal properties. (The field
marshall have a gift of speech. But he don't keep it reserved
for the club alone. He got responsibilities above and beyond
the brotherhood which is why I don't record his name. You
gotta be careful what gets put down and what don't. Everybody being watched all the time, microphones, miniature
cameras manufactured in Africa. Wherever you go they
got agents listening, keeping tabs.)

"Grease," again out of Murtagh Feud.

"Flame thrower," is exactly what I say.

Everybody at the war table looking me over then and
there, quiet, not fooling around, hearing just how I put it,
what I'm thinking. "Cook up that chicken fat."

All the club ain't present that time. 'Bout two-thirds
majority, them that's steady, dependable. Commander Fear
counting heads. The rest standing, sitting, not too formal,
still early, the secretary yet to arrive with the decoded

minutes. Commander Fear wait for quiet, then announce the count. He discharged from the Navy after the Second World War but the uniform fit anyway and he wear it proudly every week, that gold thread sewn into the cap, thick stripes on the epaulets, he look like a prime minister. Everybody out to get his attention, he don't smile much, listens hard, stays clean, gets manicured in Chattanooga where he keeps an office. Fear say to me then, "Repeat yourself, son."

"Combat flame thrower," I just say it again, holding my hands like I got the nozzle pointed, ready to go. "Cook him up."

They glance around at each other, the brothers do, nobody saying nothing much, then over in the alcove at the head of the table where the field marshall got his throne. He sit there with that hood on his features, cowl he calls it, inscribed with crosses and portents. Under the hood, the field marshal nod. There's something weird, the way he did it, give you a feeling like if a shaft of golden sunlight picked you out in the Baptist church, shined on your face to let you know you had this one special mission to fulfill.

There's times I wash my arms fifty sixty times a day. Got some kinda rash, dermatitis on my fingers, don't want it spreading. Keep it on the fingers then it don't go nowhere. Sometimes I get whatever you call them, daydreams, see it all over my body, fungus, different kinds of itch. Got to wash my arms when I see that, use special salve I get from Billy-Dick Mangle. There's gases in the air. Bacteria. Whatever Feud calls them. Noxious fumes.

Fear's the man what first told me about the world plot. It's a little bit like I knew it the whole time. Inside I got that feeling something going on all over, subversive. Niggas got their noses in it. But I don't have nothing figured till Fear come by and tell me.

Factories, he say. Engines and machines of every description. He picture it like a place where there ain't nothing but moving together, they gonna bust down them white gates, knock over the flags. It's like we're all inside, me and Commander Fear in his uniform like a prime minister, and Mangle, and Feud, all kinds of children crowding behind us like something terrible about to take place. The field marshal, though, he's already been transported somewhere safe, you can't take a chance on his sovereign person. I look at the picture. I study up the detail on the nigga face, the Jew face, I know somewheres I seen them faces before.

Fear telling me, "They left out the Catholics, son, but they're the ones built the ram."

"Keep talking, Fear." I say it 'cause I got to know.

"Hand in hand they connive. Hand in evil hand. Godless, without quarter they mean to pillage, annihilate, enslave whoever survives their initial onslaught."

"Niggas?" I put it to him. "Jews?"

"Whoever works to secure a victory for international communism." He turn and look at me through them glasses. "There is a world plot, son. A scheme in every nation made to fit the pattern of their master plan."

I put away the Springfield and sit on the window ledge. Down in the street ain't much going on. Garage where I work's just closed, some boys drinking beer, few old niggas asleep by the curb, bugs in the lamps, people rocking on porches.

"The field marshal put out that memorandum on the master plan," I say, remembering. "It come from Moscow."

He lean forward, touch me on the shoulder. "They are putting chemicals in our reservoirs, trying to drug us into apathy. They are legislating against our Constitution. They are coming by the busload to make us share our very drinking glasses with the mouths of an inferior race."

It all come out then. It's like I known it the whole while but the knowledge sealed off in a plastic sack, tied up waiting for Fear to let it out.

There's times I can't stop eating. I think how I got to stop but all the time I'm thinking, I keep it up, different kinds of whipped-cream pies and cakes, mashed potatoes with gravy, chili, red beans, Almond Joys, Sugar Daddys I buy pretending they're for some nephew, Tootsie Rolls to suck.

Doctor told me I'm too fat, gonna choke my heart.

Next meeting at the club they discuss the new buses coming in. The crisis right there in front of us. The field marshall speak out from under that cowl, show how everything relate to income tax, Supreme Courts, infiltration in government ranks, things like that. I ask about the FBI and Feud step in to say they got their hands tied. He knows. Then Mangle explain how the Army made to work against us. Everybody got some kinda report. Only the talk getting too specific. I mean I can't follow it past a point, it get all bogged down in names, numbers, facts of every description. Details ain't nothing nobody can do about all at once. Too much confusion.

Alls I saw was chicken fat. Black chicken fat got to be cleaned out. Got to be. Somebody have to be the avenging angel, swoop in from the clouds with a white-fire sword, lay the conspiracy low. One by one I talk to the other brothers, hint how I got this feeling like I been selected, picked out. They listen, they say all right, but all the while something missing, left out. They ain't committed. The field marshall working on his facts is how I figure it. Some kinda organization, everybody planning together against this subversion, nobody see how it got to be personal. Sacrifice. A hero is positively required. Too much numbers the other way, too much figures.

I watch the ceiling up over the cot at nights, fan blade making shadows, Jews and niggas driving people into mines, practicing perverse and disgusting activities. Fungus on their fingers.

Come home from the station at night, wash my arms good, use abrasive soap and disinfectant in the water. Use my weights and springs, exercise, take apart the Springfield, put it together behind my back, look for guidance. The time coming and I feel it. Makes me excited and I eat a two-pound box of pecan praline just thinking.

One day I meet Fear right after work. He's returning from some kinda meeting in Chattanooga, been there with a field marshal. He got a book which describe in detail certain sexual and social facts about the white *vs.* nigga race. It cover everything. It go right into size and smell, brain structure, glands, disease, spoilage in the blood. I read it over and over, I think of how they coming in buses trying to mess the places I eat, chewing off the same utensils, the whole while this Nicreamus Loam giving speeches agitating the whole business, speaking propaganda, no one moving to strike him down.

That's when I carry on an investigation. I find out all about this particular Nicreamus Loam. The field marshal and Feud got files, they keep records on who moves in and out. They got what they call dossiers. Photographs, fingerprints, personal information of every description, I tell you there ain't nothing left out.

The day come and I know it by the way I feel in the morning. Saturday, kinda quiet, certain excitement in the air. I get some Nehi and rye whiskey, oil the weapon, lie around the cot, break down the stock from the barrel, put the parts in my suitcase. I stroll over the nigga section.

Just stroll. Free and easy, me walking, nobody knowing the angel inside. Everything easy.

I wait in the goldenrod across from where he occupying some rented house. Two hours, maybe three, it don't sound like I can do it but I'm trained, me not moving, lying still, some kids stare but they see the avenging look and run, don't say nothing. When Loam walk up the path from his New York car, I just lay open the back of his head with half the clip, chew up his spine with the other half.

He go over, no fooling, like he hit with baseball bats. Twitch a little, bleed like a stuck pig, black-red blowing right out his ears.

College boy too, that Loam. Come from near Birmingham the dossier say, seven in the family, work North, win some scholarship in Philadelphia, place like that. All the information right there: Air Force man, first lieutenant, become a lawyer in Chicago later on, work for UNESCO, other front outfits, start out conspiracy work with CORE. Three children, would you believe it, two girls, one stud, the stud an intern, his woman got some name in books, artist, poet, like that—and me with the sword of white fire step in and stop it all dead.

You gotta think about that. Man does all those things, them hours studying up, them days advancing position, going off to meetings, getting known. Then me, I cut him down.

Didn't see Fear no more after that. Only his picture once in the paper wearing that commander uniform, gold on the cap, receiving some breed of citation.

About legal expense, the Preparation and Readiness Club got special funds for all that. Billy-Dick Mangle get some medical reports written up on account of his pharmaceutical supply store, one I live over. The field marshal work behind the scenes, can't afford to get too involved, but fix it so nothing happen for seven eight months, the courts tied up with what he call litigation. Murtagh Feud the man got to make the arrest in the first place, collect evidence, him being the local deputy, and he slow to act. So ain't nothing happen. Everything circumstantial, nobody seen me. Them that did, now what they gonna say? They gonna say they seen me?

Them that say they seen the avenging angel got to hide their eyes. The light too radiant, too strong, too pure. It come from God.

HARRY
AND THE
CELLULOID
PASSION

*This story brings to mind the feeling of cele-
bration—I think the most important thing that
could be said about Dick, or the biggest message
that he would have liked to leave behind, would
be that it's important to celebrate every minute of
living. He would have a party at the drop of a hat,
and really, most of his living hours were parties—
most of his waking hours. He dreamed a lot, too,
but I don't know what that was all about; he
wouldn't talk; he wouldn't say.*

*Of course, the partying in this story is sort of
desperate; things were pretty desperate all the time
because of the way Dick felt about what was going
on around him, in a large political-world sense, in
a small personal-private sense. With his close
friends or with people who would drop by the
house, everything affected him and a lot of it was
desperate—the way it is—and it's scary . . .*

*Kristin is probably modeled mostly after a girl
named Diane—a girl who gave Richard a copy of*
Winnie-the-Pooh *in college. All the Kristins in all
the stories are probably the same person or collection of people. A lot of people in* Been Down So
Long . . . *were modeled after real people and the
names had to be changed to protect the innocent,
you know.*

M.F.

I

Here in the baroque-and-penthoused summer world of a newly commissioned Marine (ex-South American, child of the apocalypse, soon to be shredded and torn on a distant land) was held the afternoon of the cocktail party: ceilings adorned with *putti* and angels, *Concerti Grossi* by Corelli and friends, occasional faces out of the newsreels, and the weather glorious for chilled, transparent alcohol served up in Steubenware. In the minds and hearts of all the gay young people there was ripe for removal that gray amorphous weight, that cancer of Loneliness, Menace, and Dread, which, when gone, would leave them to contemplate the worlds that still might be had, the loves that lay awaiting, the tingling diaphanous promise of vague and never-to-be-defined fulfillment left gently impressed on the brain by the proper and improper number of drinks. This was June, 1950, in the capital of Western Civilization. And swirling in the still sunflooded streets below could be seen the people who walked and drove, pulses of a kind, corpuscular movements that knocked in the veins of the streets, intangible, passing, and oh at such a glorious distance. Extend the palm in the fashion of some flamboyant magician and it would all dissolve into whatever you'd like, my dear: the sea perhaps, a field of hay, the sunspattered lake of that Swedish movie we once saw. Poof. Go away, New York. Martini again, please, with that droll little onion. So like a pearl.

In this tingling half life of siphon and ice, the arc of The Hero might possibly intersect that of His Maid. The synthesis of two private and prolonged nightmare lives (sighs against the pillow, smiles to spite the needle in the heart) might occur. An end to the day-long, life-long thought (held in abeyance, cautiously): Will I meet Her here? Is She waiting?

For Harry Genovese, Greenpoint born, Yale brought up, son of proud Abruzzi parents, out of uniform: the door opens, porkpie taken, thank you very much. The quick and semidesperate glance. Where? Then all at once, the abeyance collapsing, the last of the distance foreshortened —not here, gone, alone, oh where, and why all this, and will once more I sleep the empty night alone alone alone.

Ahem. "Is Mr. Aguilar here?"

"Yes, sir, in the kitchen. I'm sure he'll be right out."

"Ummm."

Walking over now, the windows giving out on the terrace, the circulating tray, the *ribiendo* violins, here and there a surge of laughter, strangers, some good-looking poon, that one with the orange dress— What movie? People looking . . .

"Harry, hey, no kidding, man! Good to see you come."

" 'Lo, José. The man at the door said you were in the kitchen, I was just—"

"How about some drink first, yes? What do you say, little Scotch, wasn't it?"

Not this time; distantly, the need for a drink to supplement nostalgia. The heated breeze, first of its kind, really, gentle and glorious from the terrace, echo of another time.

"Brandy, I think, José. If you've got it."

"On the table, Harry, baby." He pointed to the row of bottles and glasses standing on a Louis XIV table, amber, umber, gold, crimson, all dispensed from properly by a Chinaman in white. The doorbell tinkled: "Someone coming— Oh, and hey, man, I want later you to meet Susan Lee, you've seen her pictures?"

"Oh yes, I was just wondering . . ."

"She so digs gold braid. I told her about you a little-great lies." The bell again. "Hey, gotta run, man . . ."

José bounded off, soldier of fortune, ear deaf to his doom as Harry turned and looked again at the actress, carefully this time. But no, she was not the One. He could tell. The arc was inscribed in a separate quadrant, opposite direction, wrong polarity. Oh well. *Dum de dummm . . .* what song had come to haunt?

> *Bless 'em alll, bless 'em allll—*
> *The sergeants, an' corporals, an' allll,*
> *There'll be no promotion this side of . . .*

A face was peering at him from a chattering group of strangers. It looked again, excused itself, and walked over, a too-full drink spilling slightly at its mouth. Someone else from Yale, in the Navy program with him. No-name.

"Is Sally coming later, Harry?"

"Sally?"

"Sally Sue Pierson. From Holyoke."

Clod. "I don't think so— Maybe with someone else."

No-name realizes his blunder and looks about foolishly, acknowledging a nonexistant nod from the group he has recently left. Then, sipping at his drink like a bird in his bath, he says:

"You took the Marine option too, didn't you, Harry— you an' José?"

"That's right."

"Yeah, I remember." Another sip. "You going to that place in Virginia? Quantico?"

"In about three weeks." *Jesus.*

"Yeah. D'you hear the radio today, by the way, about that business in Korea?"

Miss Lee laughing loudly, just catching his eye. Maybe worth it for the night . . .

"Where?"

"Some island in the East. Nothing serious, probably. Still, the Marines always go first, like they say, hahaha . . ."

She looked again, winked. What the hell.

> *There'll be no promotion this side of the ocean*
> *So cheer up m' lads, bless 'em . . .*

II

Put an-other nick-el in,
In the nick-el-oh-dee-in,
Alll I want is loving you
And music, music, music . . .

"Jesus Christ, do you have to have the radio so loud?"
"It's almost five-thirty, Father; it's radio time."
"Well, it's not break-the-goddamned-chandelier-with-vibration time; please turn it down a little."

I'd do anything for you,
Anything you'd want me to,
All I want is hugging . . .

The other arc (polarity and quadrant perfect), flimsy in her peignoir, dusted and smelling of Arpège, Kristin MacLeod danced over the thickness of the hotel rug toward the radio and stuck her tongue out in the direction of the Senator's voice. *I am Moira Shearer, Pavlova someone or other, swishing in silks, dancing to death . . .*

She walked the last few steps, humming as she went, her feet sinking luxuriously into the weave, leaving padded impressions that puffed up mutely behind her. "Dum de dum de dah-de-dum . . ."

The piercing squeak of Teresa Brewer fell to a lower level.

"That's better," came the bathroom voice. Then, "Are you going out this evening, Kristin?"

"Dum de dum de— Yes, Father. As soon as I can find that crystal-ball thing."

There was a moment's silence.

"The *what?*" asked the Senator.

"The crystal . . . One of those things with the Washington Monument in it. You know, it snows when you turn it upside—Oh, never mind, it's just a joke. For José."

"Oh. That's nice, dear."

She stroked her thighs easily as she put on her stockings, and she watched the tips of her fingers. Hers? Bill's? In that other world which the plane had so marvelously left behind her as an incandescent flicker (the tilting limit of another space and time), she imagined Bill Tobin in their incense-fumed marriage chamber, the hint of a smile on his mouth as he knelt next to her quietly on the bed, his fingers reaching for her garter. Here, let me . . . Would it be like that?

He was existing in that other continuum now, breathing, pulsing, going about his business (at home, what *could* one do in the Foreign Service?), patient, confident, knowing she would return from her New York Week with a Yes. Yes, Bill Tobin, I will marry thee. Marry thee. But just now, she had her week to think, as he called it. And Bill Tobin was part of that other flicker: remote, intangible, not existing until she chose to look upon him once again. Did she love him? In time. I will learn to love thee, sweet, in the time when the leaves are dripping from the trees, when the voice of the turtle . . .

The Senator burst from the bathroom, his neck swathed in a steaming towel and a styptic pencil pressed against the shaving cut which bled thinly from his temple. He went to the telephone and asked if Mr. Austin had called yet, then hung up with a series of incoherent mutters. Many miles away a third arc had been plotted (parabola, magnitude indefinite) when the clerk in Tokyo's Dai Ichi building finally decided to call the sleeping General MacArthur and tell him that South Korea was invaded.

"Is it serious, Daddy?" Her heels were on and she studied her body in the gilded full-length mirror, stockinged, gartered, and shoed, otherwise naked under the dressing gown. *Male fetishes. French whore. Come upstairs, ducky?*

"That peninsula's the last non-Commie outpost in North Asia," he was saying. *"Serious?"*

She watched him carefully for a moment, through the mirror, as he patted the now coagulated cut and searched for a tie in the hodgepodge of his luggage. Poor Daddy. Did it mean a war, she wondered absently. (*Bill Tobin and wife in Tibet. Valiant young American couple placate fanatical followers of Dalai Lama as world watches. Picture on cover of* Life. Should she . . .)

The phone rang and the Senator answered it immediately, stiffening a little as he listened. The muted voice at the far end reached across the room to Kristin's ear, and when her father hung up, his face was changed and set.

"The Capitol," he explained. "Got to go over and see Mr. Austin." He rushed past her, finishing the tie, and slipping on his jacket and hat. "I'm sorry, Daughter," he said, "I didn't know about this before you came up to visit. If I'm not back at eight, there'll be a message at the desk and you can eat with the Williamses or some one; maybe even go back home."

"That's all right, Daddy, there's a cocktail par—" But the door had closed and he was gone.

She went to her bag and removed the directions José had written down months ago in New Haven, then, humming, took her lipstick into the bathroom. For a few hours at the least, betrothal would be allowed a corner with the other abstracts of her mind. Bill Tobin did not exist.

"Put an-other nickel in, in the nick-el-oh-dee-in . . ."

The taxi let her off at the Park Avenue number a calculated forty minutes late. She noticed two couples entering the same building and she hesitated with her fare, giving the driver a twenty-dollar bill so there would be some delay. (She wanted to arrive quite alone and there was the chance these other people were also guests.)

"What floor, miss?"

"Penthouse, please."

The elevator opened out on a small, carpeted hallway with a single door. She wondered vaguely what time it got dark and how pleasant it might be to watch the evening skyline as the lights began.

The twist bell vibrated dully between her fingers, and a young man in a blue suit answered the door. She took him to be the butler.

"Miss MacLeod," she said, looking around and taking off her gloves. "Is Mr. Aguilar here?"

"Over by the piano, ma'am."

"Ah, yes. And could you take care of this package until later, and not let me forget it?" It was the crystal ball.

"Yes, ma'am."

José Aguilar put down his drink when he saw her and came over with an exuberant smile. "Kristin," he said, *"Que tal, mi vida?"*

She took his arm in mock formality and walked back into the baroque living room, the high fashion of the guests and the sumptuous wealth of the appointments startling her momentarily.

"I'm a wreck," she answered, "but it's fun. Daddy's running around like election year, and I'm supposed to be away for a head-clearing and decision-making."

"Is someone pursuing you? Give me his name and I'll have him killed."

"Oh, I'll tell you about it later; can I get a drink?"

"There's one coming behind you."

Kristin turned to find two martinis being offered by the man who had taken the crystal ball at the door.

"Ma'am," he said with a faint smile.

She knew her mistake at once.

"You don't know this one here," José said with a very Latin gesture of the hand, happy and affected, "my very best friend in the world, this Harry. Harry Genovese—Kristin MacLeod."

"Hello, Mr. Genovese, I'm afraid I owe you—"

"That's all right. Which one?" he asked, holding up both glasses. "This is Gordon's and this is Beefeater."

"Beefeater," she said. "Sounds like more fun."

She looked at him over the rim of her raised glass and found his eyes watching hers with disarming intensity. He

looked, she decided, rather like Lord Byron with short
hair. But there was a touch of anxiety in his countenance—
the faintest glimmer, hardly more than a suspicion, of *The
Stranger*. It prevented her from smiling. It was also the
most immediate and unrestrained invitation to intimacy she
had ever known.

III

Before the hour of four o'clock on this afternoon of the
cocktail party, Harry Genovese had occupied his time by
wandering without purpose through the streets of New
York City. The chambers of his mind, otherwise inert, were
echoing with nostalgia (undefined, Romantic) for some
other place and time. Were he asked for more precise con-
figurations, he would have assigned the decade following
1920 and let it go at that. He had just received his orders
(heretofore a tenuous abstract) and was depressed.

The instructions were too calculated and austere. They
implied disciplined limbo, a splice in the tape of meaningful existence. Even if there were a war—and the conditions
hardly seemed favorable—the gay abandon of the century's
first great conflict would be lacking. No groups would
gather to sing the old club songs before going off with an
ambulance corps to France or Italy. The A.A.S. and
Nörten-Harjes were faded from the land, and with them
had gone the men who pledged one another's blood in the
roaring bistros and jogged about in the great clanking
trucks of olive drab. Glorious irresponsibility, the sublimely
spectatorial attitude in the wake of someone else's war—
these would not be had again. There had intervened somewhere in a period of chaotic time from which he, Harry
Genovese, declared himself exempt, The Insensitive Onslaught Machine, and the bomb. It seemed very much that
the great old times were gone. As for Korea, he had heard
mention of some difficulty or other that morning on the
radio. He dismissed it easily, mistaking it for a kind of

religious indigestion that always seemed a plague to those little Eastern principalities.

The feeling of nostalgia he could not dismiss, however, and eventually he succumbed, courting it with absent pauses by the statue of Prometheus in the patio at Rockefeller Center, and with a full hour over a bottle of English ale at the Café de la Paix, watching the horse-drawn hansom cabs in the blooming Central Park. Life, he reflected between pauses and sips, was all an absurdly pointless motion picture. His four preceding years were as the mist in a Japanese montage, without incident, serene, and far away. He felt older than his years. He was alone. Oh well.

He brought the oppressive weight of this solitude to the cocktail party, almost wearing it as a sign upon his forehead. The first drink softened the reverie, however, and despite a conscious effort to exacerbate it with the next, he achieved only a dim and distant self-awareness of mutability. He needed a woman. He was a soldier off to . . . well, to somewhere. He still was unaware of the quadrant of his arc and its perilous inclination toward the axis inscribed that morning in Korea . . .

"Where?"

"Some island in the East. Nothing serious, probably. Still, the Marines always go first, like they say, hahaha . . ."

The actress looked again in his direction, winked. What the hell . . . He excused himself from No-name and went over toward her group near the terrace. They were talking show business.

"Thought people gots parts by sleeping with the director," a sun-glassed blonde was asking.

"Only in France," replied Susan Lee, her eye on Harry, "in America you have to make it with the producer."

There was laughter, some of it genuine, and Lieutenant Genovese was back with the world.

"Suppose you've got talent?" he asked.

"Baby, *everybody's* got talent. But how're the picture boys gonna know?"

"An agent?" he offered.

"The agent has to make it with the make-up man."

There was more laughter and José walked over, a bottle of smuggled absinthe for the bar in his hands. The rest of the group continued joking above his greeting.

"Special delivery," he said, indicating the bottle. "From Cuba. Oh, and hey, man, did you get your orders yet?"

"Yesterday." Then in a whisper, "What do you know about this actress here?"

"Susie? She took an act to Bogotá last year when I was home. Bad show, but she likes to mix it up between numbers. You want to get some? She's expensive."

"After the crowd breaks up. I'm not good at this show talk. And you can lend me some bread."

"Tell her you dig her movies and have Russian blood. "She's a little on the left and loves assassins."

"Really?"

"So who wants an Oscar?" Susan was saying. "Walt Disney gets Oscars."

The group broke up after some of the ensuing jokes got stale, and its various members drifted off to other sections of the living room. At a signal from Harry, José came over and made the introductions.

"You're in the theatre?" she asked.

"Marine Corps," said Harry. "Same thing."

She found the remark hilarious and almost choked on the cocktail frankfurter placed in her mouth by a passing producer. Dinner at Lüchow's was arranged.

People continued to join the party around them and almost no one left. The warm summer breeze was infectious with good feeling, the bottles and glasses tinkled gaily with the chatter of talk, and everyone seemed to be in much the same libertine mood. José Aguilar gave instinctive ground to The American Way, and was becoming drunk with the guests. From a battery of speakers all over the many rooms of the penthouse, the musical duel of the *Concerti Grossi* tumbled and flowed.

After the third Tom Collins (it was a question of thirst now, and not ritual), Harry still felt dry, disappointingly sober, and in need of something more potent. He was on his way to a chilled and very dry Manhattan when he heard the front doorbell ringing beside him and he looked out into the hall.

It was a young woman smelling of Arpège. Their eyes met momentarily and she said, "Miss MacLeod." Then she gave him a small cube-shaped package and asked would he not let her forget it when she left. He was apparently the butler so he said, Yes, ma'am.

The intersection of the arcs. As she walked toward the piano and José, she left him in a state similar to that of the man who has dreamed something vague and intangible about capital just before inheriting three million dollars from an unknown aunt. All day in the shadow of Romantic intuition, he was shocked in the presence of its probable source. The Love of his Life had just looked at him and walked into the next room. And at the stunned moment of standing there with her gloves and package in his hands, he wondered what to do about it. He brought her two martinis.

"For Miss MacLeod," he said when he had found her. Her expression changed at once.

"You don't know this one here," José said with a flamboyant wave of the hand, "my very best friend in the world, this Harry. Harry Genovese—Kristin MacLeod."

He parried her attempt at apology, gave her a choice of gins, and watched her expression with passionate intensity.

José was confused. "Do you two know each other?"

Kristin explained, they all laughed, and there was a general move to the terrace. A warm breeze was blowing in gentle gusts from the Hudson and the evening air was filled with the diluted scent of the distant ocean. It was possible to see certain lights popping on in the buildings downtown, and except for the glow in the west, the sky was a semidark transparent blue, almost the color of dawn.

Venus, just passing the zenith, was mistaken for a large star by Harry and wished upon silently. A *sonata da chiesa* proclaimed itself from the single outdoor speaker, and momentarily the *ribiendo* regained its musical advantage. Standing there silently, with the knowledge that the unknowing pulses in the street below could be retained or dissolved by a magician's gesture, Kristin and Harry had an interlocking epiphany, a simultaneous sense of magic and motion about to be entered upon, if one could but find the key.

"Are you hungry, Kris?" asked José. "We have shrimp hors d'oeuvre from Bo-Bo's and special ersatz hot dogs."

"Famished," she said.

"Oh, and get me a Manhattan while you're there, would you, José?" asked Harry. "Dry . . . twist of lemon."

There were some moments of self-conscious silence when the host had gone, but they faded easily as Harry remembered something of Kristin's history from talks in New Haven.

"Will you be in town long?" he asked.

"Two weeks, I think. It depends on Daddy . . . You?"

"Less than a month now. José and I go to Quantico about the same time."

"Ah, you're in the Marines too?"

"Afraid so."

Another pause as some laughter surged out of the living room and the *tutti* faltered in the presence of the trio sonata. Harry sighed, looking out toward the river.

"It's really something here, isn't it?"

"Yes," she said, "lovely."

"It doesn't seem"—he struggled for the proper word— "well, it's not . . . *real* somehow . . . don't you think?"

She was looking away at the blinking light on the Empire State building as he asked, the martini glass just touching her lips. He watched her carefully as she turned and nodded without speaking, her teeth gripping the edge of the Steuben rim. (Gone Bill Tobin, to the winds, Tibet, some other land, and freedom now, a last love to lose . . .)

She extended her hand gracefully, deliberately, pausing just once with delicate poise, and touched it to his own.

They were still looking into each other's eyes when José came back with the drink, and a small plate of food with toothpicks.

"How'd you make out with Susan?" he asked.

Harry looked up suddenly, remembering. Kristin watched him. "Dinner," he said hoarsely. He thought a minute. "Why don't you two join us?"

"I don't think so," said José. "Kristin's no doubt tired from shopping and all that, and I . . ."

(The fading coal, lost, alone . . .)

"Why don't we?" she asked quickly.

Harry stepped gracefully on his host's foot, without a change of expression.

"Do you want to?" asked José.

"Why not? It might make Washington that much further away."

"Fine then. Harry, you're sure Susan won't mind?"

"Susan loves people," he said.

One drink more for each of them, an earnest and fraternal good-bye from No-name, a quick return for the almost forgotten crystal ball, and they all tumbled out into the night. Susan hailed a taxicab by baring a leg to the thigh. Lüchow's was sacrificed for Minetta's, in Greenwich Village, where they would not have to speak in hushed tones. Cinzano, dinner with wine (Pouilly-Fuissé, redeeming to the senses), cheese, more cocktails. A spontaneous song from Susan about illicit love among the pachyderms, applause from the clientele. Kristin abandoning diplomatic care to the electricity of the atmosphere. A few recognized theatre friends and the group expands to eight. MacDougal Street, the San Remo; Sixth Avenue, Mona's; Sheridan Square, Louie's; Hudson Street, the White Horse. The evening spun and swirled around them, all the gay young people, red lights, popping flashbulbs, taxicabs, "The Marine Hymn," a scene from Susan's picture, a Spanish song from José . . . the key had been found. Keeping to one drink per bar, they all

avoided unconsciousness, José dozing a little in taxis. A
final attempt to keep the night alive! Susan's apartment?
No liquor. The Café de la Paix? Closed. A hansom cab
through the park? Yes, of course, how square, but of course!
. . . Dying laughter, a series of heaving sighs, and finally just
the clip-clopping of hooves from the pavement, echoing
into the silent night. In whispers:
  "I don't know about tomorrow, Harry. Daddy might
want . . ."
  "As soon as possible then, all right? I've got to see you,
Kristin."
  Clip clop clip clop clip clop . . .
  "Do you?"
  "I'll call."
  "No, let me . . ."
  "All right . . ."

IV

  The glorious groves of Hypocrisy. Still the movie, pointless and absurd. Waiting for her call the following day, he
half expected the megaphonic voice of some cosmic director
to boom out over the set, OK, Genovese, but try belying
the rehearsals. Miss MacLeod—a little better, but watch
the underplaying, we have to have *some* idea what you're
thinking. All right, Manny, a little lower camera this time,
and let's take it from where the doorbell rings . . .
  He played it again in his mind, ran it from doorbell to
Susan's unconscious good night, added a little here, took
some away. But there remained only the one epiphanal
moment, a stasis of absolute self-knowledge that was dissipated and lost as the hansom cab moved on. Susan had
turned away and was trying to pull the bearskin up over
her shoulders, mumbling, "Shit, it's cold for June," just
loud enough to hear. José was snoring. Kristin had Harry's
jacket half on, and was turning up the collar with her face
not six inches from his own. When they kissed, she held

his lower lip between her teeth and a soft whimper of passion escaped from her throat. It came and went, poof, she tucked her chin against her bosom, closed her eyes, and that was all. How many nightmare sighs, he wondered, are sighed against the pillow before a sound like that might be abandoned into the night? It haunted him.

"Wanna come up for a nightcap, baby?" Susan had whispered.

"I thought you were out of liquor."

clip clop clip clop . . .

"Jus' about 'nough for two li'l drinks . . ."

Kristin had crossed her arms in front of her, her hands holding her own shoulders, and was watching him carefully. Her expression said *There's time. We can wait.*

Lord, the unwaited times gone by . . . the Memory Serene polluted with incident: hot breath in the ear, the softness of a leg where the nylon ends and the flesh begins, the rubbing of thighs through two layers of clothes: wrong, foul, a hideous violation, oh, the clever, clever little girls gone by . . .

I'm sorry I wore a girdle, darling.

That's all right, Sally.

I won't wear one next time.

Mmm.

What time is it?

Watch is on my left hand. You're—

Here I'll move . . . I'd hate to be late and get in trouble.

Unhh . . . twelve-thirty.

Twelve-thirty?

Yep.

Maybe I'd better . . . Oh, Harry, don't do that . . . Harry, please, darling . . . ohhhh . . . *damn* this girdle anyway!

Damn Sally Sue Pierson. Fumbling in her underclothing. How much mortification for one messy pant-wetting orgasm.

Kristin, Kristin, lovely Kristin, far from all that, who'll bring tea to the fields, my love my life my lost and dying once-forever days . . . there's time . . . we can wait . . .

The phone was ringing.

"Hello?"

"May I speak to Mr. Genovese, please?"

"Kris?"

"I didn't wake you, did I?"

"I've been up about ten minutes. What time is it?"

"It's—Hold on a minute . . . twenty of one."

"Well?"

"Well . . ."

"When do I pick you up?"

"Oh, Harry, do you think you ought to? I mean I—"

"Yes."

"Well . . ."

"I'll be there at four. No, three . . ."

"Do you know where I'm staying?"

"Le George Cinq?"

"What?"

"Nothing. Do you like daiquiris?"

At the Café de la Paix they sat at the small sidewalk table and watched the people strolling by on Fifty-ninth Street. They were sipping frozen daiquiris, looking occasionally into each other's eyes and smiling. It was all very pleasant. During the walk over from the Plaza, Kristin had talked briefly of Korea and he allowed the name a personal notch in his consciousness so that a dash of genuine mutability was added to the salad of their afternoon. They both behaved and talked as if the previous evening had occurred months before.

"Do you generally drink so early in the day, Harry?"

"It's almost cocktail hour. Tradition and all that."

"Harry?"

"Umm?"

"You're preoccupied."

"Really?"

"Now don't be fresh."

He took a sip from the daiquiri, then licked away the

ice clinging to his upper lip. Kristin was absently watching a mounted policeman cross from Sixth Avenue into the park.

"What are you thinking?" she asked.

"Lousy casting," he muttered.

"What?"

"I feel like I'm in a goddamned movie."

"Shhh."

"OK."

She watched the horse until it was lost in traffic.

"The timing's off, anyway," she said. "By rights you should have met me last year, had me visit once or twice in New York, then come to Washington."

"Oh?"

"But only on weekends. You'd take me to country-club dances and fall in love with sister. She'd throw you over, of course, but by then I'd be married to some successful young man in the Foreign Service." She took a drink from her glass, watching him over the rim. "Then I'd be unfaithful and we'd take a trailer near Quantico."

"I like the last part."

"It's not finished. The State Department would send my husband to Tibet."

"Banishment?"

"Of a sort. But I wouldn't go."

"What then?"

"You'd desert the Marines and we'd come and live in Greenwich Village and go back to all the places we saw last night."

"I'd grow a beard."

"And I'd become an actress."

A light changed from red to green and there was the sudden sound of traffic moving. A horn or two, a clutch let out quickly, a policeman's whistle.

"This is ridiculous, Kristin."

"I know."

There had existed, felt Harry, right from the time of the

doorbell, the kind of nonsensory understanding that would only come full circle in the senses. The consummation had begun and there was no avoiding its synthesis. *There's time. We can wait.*

The following morning, all military leaves were canceled. Disaster had entered the room and quietly taken a chair in the corner.

He called the Fifth Avenue Hotel in Greenwich Village almost at once and ordered a suite for Mr. and Mrs. Genovese. A pseudonym would have been unthinkable.

But the nightmare voice at the Plaza told him something quite impossible. Miss MacLeod had checked out with her father. Who was calling please? Oh yes, Mr. Genovese, she tried to reach you last night, late. You're to call her in Washington.

The second call was long in answering. Yes, Kristin had returned home, who was this? Genovese, Lieutenant Genovese? No, this is the Senator. She'll be back later tonight. Why don't you call person to person?

More of the movie. The sound track amplified the muted voice at the far end of the wire. Only certain words were clear. Kristin, Bill Tobin, and Marriage. Off somewhere making plans. Couldn't have made better choice. Was Lieutenant friend of Bill's?

Disaster, a leer hidden beneath the veil that covered its face, had risen from the chair to tap Harry Genovese on the shoulder.

V

Open on medium C.U. of drunk Marine lieutenant carefully descending Fifth Avenue steps of Plaza Hotel. Doorman salutes him and he begins inspection of doorman's uniform. Sound: Evening traffic noises, hansom cab, hoofbeats, etc. Second Marine descends steps with two actresses. One is drunk and wears a gold sequin dress. She gestures theatrically and does Charleston steps. Sound: Fade in old

*tinny record of Charleston music and hold under. Dolly
back to entire group from beyond Plaza fountain. Drunk
Marine has abandoned inspection. He takes off jacket and
stumbles toward camera in direction of fountain. Others
laugh. Charleston girl removes shoes and follows as second
Marine looks for taxi.*

DRUNK MARINE *(Singing over Charleston music)*

> *By the shee, by the shee,*
> *By a' beautiful shee-*
> *Youn'me, youn'me*
> *Oh how happy'll be . . .*

*(Hold song under. Cut to C.U. second Marine looking down
Fifth Avenue in horror. Drunk Marine continues raving
loudly)*

DRUNK MARINE *(Raving loudly)* Shusan . . . SHUSAN!

(SUSAN *dances over without shoes, places finger
atop head of drunk Marine, and dances umbrella-fashion
around him)*

DRUNK MARINE Shusan baby, we're going for a li'l dip.
Take off clothes.

❧   *(Dolly back from C.U. to second Marine running
toward them, gesturing emphatically at place where he had
looked in horror. Other actress is getting in taxi)*

DRUNK MARINE I think Misser Aguilar's tryin' tell us somethin'.

(Middle-distance shot of SUSAN *removing stockings.
Drunk* MARINE *sits on edge of fountain and helps. He lifts
back dress and begins to unhook devices. Zoom C.U. drunk*
MARINE *gently nibbling* SUSAN *on upper thigh. Pull back,*
SUSAN *offering other leg. Sound: Increase volume Charleston music as second* MARINE *reaches them and points in
horror at MPs in Fifth Avenue distance. All three scramble
to taxi,* SUSAN *making obscene gestures in direction of MPs.
Dolly back as taxi pulls away from curb, then stops. Hold
camera position as door opens and drunk* MARINE *stumbles
back for pair of* SUSAN's *shoes lying on sidewalk. He fills*

one from hip-pocket flask and drinks casually. Taxi backs up and various hands pull him in back seat. Taxi pulls away. Follow taxi with full-focus lens as it merges with other Fifth Avenue traffic. Pan slowly to Plaza fountain and hold, as hansom cab goes by in middle distance. Sound: Fade up Charleston music. Cut to plush actress-type bedroom. Oversized bed covered by large white bearskin. Angora rugs, great fat pillows, etc. Many telephones. Mirrors. Open liquor cabinet. Adjoining bathroom. Over bed hangs Picasso painting of bull making love to water sprite. Sound: Muffled party sounds, tinkling glasses, laughter, etc., all through closed door. Dolly back to MARINE's *jacket over back of vanity chair,* SUSAN's *gold sequin dress on floor. Pan slowly to thirty-degree mirror shot revealing drunk* MARINE *in flowered underpants pouring self drink. He sings)*
DRUNK MARINE *(Over party sounds)* "There's a rose 'at grows in no-man's land, An he's beautiful to seee . . ."

(He stops singing, takes drink and grins sheepishly at self in mirror. Expression changes to one of extreme concentration. He lifts glass formally and offers toast to mirror)
DRUNK MARINE To los' times an' vanished regimes. *(Pauses, drinks and toasts again)* To a continued well being of Miss Kris'in MacLeod. *(Pauses, drinks again, repeats self absently)* My los' an' only . . .
(Sound: Opening door of adjoining bedroom, C.U. mirrorshot over drunk MARINE's shoulder showing SUSAN walking across room in shortie nightgown and bikini panties. She stumbles slightly. On nightgown, over left breast, is small Marine pin. Pull back for full mirror shot of drunk MARINE kissing SUSAN on lips, neck, shoulders, and just below Marine pin. Squirming. Drop camera angle to show only couple's legs from middle thighs down. Bikini panties fall to floor. Flowered underpants fall to floor. Sound: Giggling whispers, etc. Shortie nightgown falls to floor. C.U. shot of feet turning and walking across Angora rug to bed. Sound: Main bedroom door opening, feet stop and face

door. Sound: Louder party noises. Hold camera on feet)
LIEUTENANT AGUILAR *(Voice Offstage)* Oh, excuse me.
I didn't know . . .
DRUNK MARINE Now you know.
SUSAN When you leave, feel free to lock a'door affer you.
        (Extreme C.U. of feet mounting three small steps
to bed)
LIEUTENANT AGUILAR *(Officially)* Plane's at eleven, Harry,
you've got two hours.
DRUNK MARINE Sure thing.
SUSAN G'night, Misser Aguilar.
        Sound: Door closing. Extreme C.U. feet tickling
each other. General foot play, etc. Pan to night light as two
hands reach for switch. Pan to Picasso painting. Hold on
painting as lights go out. Then pan across thrashing forms
in bed to door from which light leaks. Dolly in slowly to
door, bringing up party sound. Voices singing the "Marine
Hymn." Cross fade to old recording)
SOUND *(With slight echo)* Oh the long and the short and
    the tall.
There'll be no promotion
This side of the ocean . . .

BOLD
MARAUDER

Azamat, without question, an international con man . . . Taking me to the party at Stephen Spender's just after the Edinburgh Festival. Asking, "What do you want to be for these people, Dick, a writer or a musician?"

A musician, of course. Removes me from the competitive circuit, allows for confidential asides! Oh, la.

(from RICHARD FARIÑA's diary)

It's hi, ho, hey, I am the Bold Marauder
    and hi, ho, hey, I am the white destroyer.
For I will buy you silver and gold
    and I will bring you treasure.
And I will bring a widowing flag
    and I will be your lover.
And I will show you grotto and cave
    and sacrificial altar,
And I will show you blood on the stone,
    and I will be your mentor.
And night will be our darling
    and fear will be our name.

It's hi, ho, hey, I am the Bold Marauder
    and hi, ho, hey, I am the white destroyer.
For I will take you out by the hand
    and lead you to the hunter,
And I will show you thunder and steel
    and I will be your teacher.
And we will dress in helmet and sword
    and dip our tongues in slaughter
And we will sing a warrior's song
    and lift the praise of murder.
And Christ will be our darling
    and fear will be our name.

It's hi, ho, hey, I am the Bold Marauder
    and hi, ho, hey, I am the white destroyer.
For I will sour the winds on high
    and I will burn the grain in the fields
    and I will be your mother.
And I will go to ravage and kill
    and I will go to plunder,

And I will take a fury to wife
and I will be your father.
And death will be our darling
and fear will be our name.

THE WRITER AS
CAMERAMAN

Carrying a camera on your shoulder or having a camera in your mind—people really do it.

This piece was supposed to go into the newspaper in San Francisco because Dick was going to come up and give a talk, or a party, or whatever—a celebration!—for his book coming out. It was an invitation, really, for people to come and talk to him and ask whatever questions they felt like about the book. I like the thought . . .

As for Plastic Man, *Dick just loved all that weirdness, cartoon-craziness; he really had that great sense of mush!*

I have an odd feeling that they've met by now, he and Plastic Man *and all the rest. I hope they're having a good laugh.*

M.F.

There used to be times when writing was like acting for Panavision. When mirror-conscious me was too intensely aware of the camera dollying about the room; studying posture at the Smith-Corona; zooming closeups on a passionately raised eyebrow; recording fingertips whenever they drummed reflective pauses on a vintage copy of, say, *Plastic Man*. Call it all a hangup.

But the cameraman was me as well. Perhaps more of a writer-type than somber Richard at the keys, blowing smoke through his teeth as if he were Jean-Paul Belmondo. And the producer, the director, the continuity man, the chap who scored on the script girl with a promise of a small but significant part in the second reel, all me, split four or five ways like a Marx Brothers molecule gone aesthetic in an atomic age.

It was like that for too long, years in fact, and while it continued, the hangup provided me with authentic-looking heroes, publication in the usual literary quarterlies, and invitations to very whispery cocktail parties. Except that the heroes were sculpted from water and sand, nobody *really* read the quarterlies, and the cocktail parties were a full drag.

So I bought a one-way ticket to Europe and North Africa, where in due course I learned how to annihilate the camera and kiss a sweet good-bye to the crew that went with it. There were two winters in England, one in France, another in Tangier, two in Paris; assorted springs and autumns, and a busted marriage, all propped up by the copper wages of streetsinging, coffeehouse hoofing, bit parts in transient flicks, and the going rate for what I choose to call High Adventure.

The Algerian war was on, cafés in the Quarter were being machine-gunned, bookstores were regularly bombed, Arabs were found hanging each morning in the Bois de

Boulogne, and while a buddy of mine was strolling across
the Boulevard St. Michel, telling me about the coming in-
fluence of Bo Diddley on Liverpool mods, he was stabbed
by a giggling maniac in a fez, and he didn't know it until
he got to our hotel. What can I tell you?

Been Down So Long It Looks Like Up to Me was
started in a room on the rue St. André des Arts, some four
hours after I'd finished work as a blind harmonica player.
It was about three years since I'd left the States and the
camera was no longer to be found. And if it could have
been, it didn't matter, because I wasn't looking. And if I
was looking, nobody would have told me where it was. And
if they had, they would have been lying.

So I was able to finish the book in California, between
Carmel and Big Sur, in a one-room cabin with nobody
watching but Mimi, the girl I'd brought back from Paris,
and she wasn't watching so much as she was dancing or
weaving modal memories on the guitar. One of the points
being that without the bloody camera bobbing around, I
could take daily trips into the heads and activities of the
book's people, chart their respective journeys, plot their
curves, and structure their involvements without the dis-
traction of some other casting director. If you follow.

Resolving this conflict between Inside and Outside (micro
and macrocosm) is, incidentally, precisely what motivates
the book's central character. For the teachers who call that
conflict obscure, I recommend the theories of solar origin
on page 237. For the prudes who find the sex overt, I
recommend the calculus on page 106. For the Minutemen
who suspect subversion in the hedonism of the protagonist,
please turn to the German's short analysis of the third dimension. All other questions should be saved for Sunday,
May 1, at the Discovery Bookstore in North Beach, where
together with Big Frederick Roscoe, the owner, I promise
to look for answers among the store's collection of ceramic
heads. Who knows, in another incarnation, maybe one of
them was a cameraman.

LITTLE
NOTHING
POEMS

Dick thought up most of these late in the night and would turn over and write them. He'd read his writing on-and-off during the day; then, when he'd go to bed, he'd be free to think of more nothing. For about a two-week period we were thinking about nothing. Driving along in the car, he would remember one and I'd have to write it down. The last one he wrote down for me.

M.F.

The author, who had precisely
nothing
on his mind when he wrote
these poems, would like
to thank his publishers
for finding all
the necessary space.

Nothing
does it
like 7-Up.
And you don't
have to pay
a deposit
either.

Nothing
can take the place
of a blue-eyed baby boy
from Shaker Heights, Ohio,
full of strained asparagus.
When he's all grown up
and wears Bermuda shorts,
the figures say
his future is secure.
But on the other hand,
nothing
can take his place.

Ornette Coleman
at the Five Spot
when it came his turn
to play a twelve-bar
measure, smiled serenely
    at the crowd
and fingered nothing
on his plastic horn.
He feels more nothing
than you know.

If captured
by the enemy
tell them
nothing
but your name
and rank and
maybe number.
Even if it makes
you feel embarrassed.

Nothing
twisted Einstein's head
as much as where
it ended.
And it just might,
thank you.

When congratulated
by the press
after paddling,
belly downward,
from San Carlos to Malibu,
a distance of four hundred
and eleven miles,
on a surfboard,
the lifeguard told them,
"It was nothing."
But they ran the story
all the same.

"That's nothing,"
said Plastic Man,
after watching
a kid from Tokyo
go seventeen feet
over the top
with a fiberglass pole.
But those little
bitty television
sets were just starting
to corner the market
and the State Department
shut him up
with of all things
a Scotch tape substitute
they're turning out
in Yokohama.

There is nothing
like a dame.
And there's more
of it around.

Nothing
could put
Humpty Dumpty
together again.
But there was a war on
so they had to try
all those other things.

"If there's anything
I can do to help,"
said Ben Casey.
"Nothing,"
sobbed the young British widow,
adjusting her shades.
"I'm sorry," he told her.
"Perhaps in your own country.
But here, it's not
on the Blue Cross."

Harry Jackson
lived on nothing
until a critic
from *Art News*
explained how
it really wasn't
feasible
in a fully employed
society;
and the poor fellow
had to flee
to Italy.

Nothing
is quite as exclusive
as this year's full-fashion
cabaña-wear wardrobe
from St. Laurent's
private showroom
on the Quai d'Orsay.
And you're far more likely
to get your picture
in *Playboy*
or one of those other
magazines.

Piglet
had a way of finding
nothing
in a hole
and calling it a Heffalump
instead.
He knew more nothing
than you or I.

I've got plenty of
nothing.
But then
so do most people
in my position.

Nothing
succeeds like success;
and you don't have to come on
as much
around the office,
do you?

Paul
would have been
nothing
without his wife.
But they were inseparable,
so he never knew
what he missed,
so to speak.

In the beginning
there was nothing.
A rather difficult
scene to make,
if you dig.

Charlie Chan
had nothing
much to go on,
really,
but with Number One
Son always hanging around
it was the only clue
he needed.

Nothing
is worse,
said Elsa Maxwell,
not long before
her passing,
Than being alone.
Even though her scene was pretty
crowded
to begin with.

Nothing
would have changed
the mind
of the Planter's Peanut Man,
who stood weeping
on the ledge
of the Chrysler Building.
The police tried
talking to him
instead,
so he jumped,
leaving only his
monocle
as a token
of affection
to the world
behind.

Nothing
is good enough
for those who know.
Providing
someone takes the time
to pass the word.

Ever catch yourself
looking at the wallpaper
thinking about
nothing?
It happens to everyone
these days.
If you all got
together
and started a club,
it wouldn't take you
very far.

She whispered sweet
nothings
in his ear
but he was always
a little too straight
to pick up what
she was laying down
and he never
got much.

There's nothing
to do
on a rainy day
in Nebraska,
but it stays dry
and you never get
the chance.

Nothing
matters any more.

POEM FOR A WOMAN WHO LOVED

This was an old poem or, at least, it was already published when I met Dick. I used to worry who the girl was: Maybe it's Kristin, I thought. Now I just like the poem.

I really bugged Dick about why he said at the beginning of Been Down So Long . . . , "This one is for Mimi." "Why did you say that?" I said. "Who is the next one going to be for?"

M.F.

Spent and done, she fell away with no more sound
than what the bangles whispered at her wrist.
The feral tumbling nights that sang among her joys
rolled in silence now and roared no more.
While all the winking crystal of the noonday stars
could bring no light to eyes that failed to see.
The bronze and shimmering young sons of naked gods
had risen in their turn, with neither curse
nor benediction on their gilded lips,
and opened restless wings among the typhooned skies.
Smiling (in their turn) they reeled away,
leaving little but a blinded, aging moon
which bore no human company. Alone
she traced her sunning thighs with anxious fingers,
dreaming of the ceilings that she'd known.

THE PASSING OF VARIOUS LIVES

I love the mood in this particular story! Dick wrote it before he got to be so "funny cynical" —which was kind of a drag sometimes. But this took me right off my feet and plunked me in the middle of his story—great! He lived in Cuba for some time as a child—I never really knew exactly what he did when he went down there (from college) to fight in the hills, or whatever it was he was supposedly going to do. Sometimes I didn't know the difference between his fantasy and his reality—he would tell me something he had done and I kind of had to nod and wonder or pick up what I could from other conversations, because he couldn't help exaggerating so.

There are a lot of Dick's relatives in this story, I think, and a lot of family feeling that doesn't come across in anything else that he wrote—except maybe in "Birthday." The feeling of having family around doesn't show up too much in his writing—and it's such a good feeling . . .

M.F.

I

JULY 1942

The summers at Varadero were far easier to pass than those of Cuba's interior. The air was warm, sometimes hot in the afternoons; but it was a pleasant heat, soothed by the sea breezes which, if they were not cool, at least served to keep the air from becoming stagnant and heavy. The houses, some of them still under construction, were situated at great distances from each other and were built atop the bluffs that rose some twenty to thirty feet above the level of the sea. In the early mornings it was possible to watch the fishermen setting out in their small boats. But most of the people who lived in the new houses only saw them as they returned in the evenings, their craft heavier then, and moving slowly.

The houses presented a strong contrast to the shacks used by the fishermen, since they were built by men who came from other parts of Cuba and who had made a great deal of money. Some of them were Americans, but only a few. There was a hotel close to the fishing shacks, and the accommodations were comfortable, if not good.

At the northern end of a particularly attractive stretch of beach, one which was favored because it turned sharply and made a view of the fishing shacks difficult, there stood two houses very close together. One had been there for some years and was the property of the retired chief engineer of the sugar mill at Jatibo. The other was very new and belonged to his son. Until recently, both houses had been used only in the summers, but now the older one,

called Casa Elena after the chief engineer's wife, was used
almost all year round, since Elena preferred the refreshing
air of the sea to the dust of the mill town. Her tastes were
very precise and she had had the house finished according
to her own specifications. This particular summer, however,
she was disturbed. On the first day of July, her mother-
in-law had come to Varadero and was now staying at the
hotel. The woman was old, near eighty, and had not re-
covered from the shock of her husband's death some months
before. She was almost blind from cataracts, and had to
be helped everywhere. Each day, she sat on the porch
facing the sea she had never seen, watched the boats go
in and out, and moaned softly to herself. Elena was terrified
that the old woman, Laudelina, would die before the summer was out and create great amounts of confusion.

But neither confusion nor Elena troubled the old woman.
She was very near death, of course, but this time it was
her own end that approached, and what went on after its
occurrence was of little concern to her. She had a reason
to remain alive (a son she wanted to see), and until then
she would be patient and think thoughts of the town she
had never been apart from until that June.

At her home in Jatibo, there was no sea. Nor were there
any gentle hills or valleys that might help a breeze swing
down through the town. There was only a great flatness,
a dusty unbroken plain that stretched without change to
every horizon. The air was thick and still in the summer
months, inhabited mostly by flies or mosquitoes that hung
drowsily about, waiting for some convenient arm or neck
on which to poise. There was the Central Highway, built
by Machado, which brought the buses and provided for
the little hotel and *bodega* beneath it. And there was the
sugar mill, with its steady pounding drone that seemed not
at all out of place in the drugging heat. From the mill,
without which the town would not have existed, came the
strong throat-filling smell of the hot sugar as it passed
through the last stages of breakdown from the cane. And
the harvesters and mill hands shuffled slowly between the

company-owned houses and their jobs, wide-brimmed straw hats pulled down close to their eyes.

Laudelina (or Abuela, as she was called now) sat and considered those days that seemed, for some reason, to exist in another person's life. She could not comprehend this sensation of distance more, since she had lived in the town for all of her almost eighty years. But now, sitting and rocking on the porch of the hotel, she felt like a stranger to that town. The days there swung through her mind with great speed, not like these of such length in Varadero. Her girlhood was a gentle blur, her parents hardly visible in the depths of her brain. Life had only begun with old Joaquin, her husband, who was a blacksmith at the mill. (The thought of him left her weak.) Then had come Raul, the first son, and the others in their time. There had been nineteen children, sixteen of whom had lived. And even though she could find no reason for not thinking of each birth, each childhood as separate and distinct, her mind failed her as her eyes and many of them came together in her head, making her forget the names. Raul, of course she remembered, he was the oldest—it was his house that she stayed near now. And Joaquinito, the youngest, he was her favorite. Slighter than the others, and good-looking. Still, the thought of him gave her pain; why was he not there now?

The others came to mind now and again: Francisco, named for her father; Laudelina, the first daughter—named for herself; Paolo, who survived the yellow fever; Cecelia, the prettiest; Manuel, who now sold Bacardi in Santiago; Humberto, the darkest; Consuela, who was fat and happy and brought lunch to her father at the mill; Tomás, who was the hardest birth; Alberto, who lost an eye . . . but that was only—how many? Ten? No, eleven. There were five more. What were their names? They were her children, she should not forget.

Still, there were reasons for her forgetting. And these reasons were folded deep into the wrinkles that lined her face. They lived in little flashes behind her clouded eyes and brought the faces and names of children who were not her own, but whom she had brought into the world. The records clerk in Jatibo, along with many of the mill hands and farmers, spoke of how she had delivered almost nine hundred children in her time. They remembered her firm unfailing step whenever she left her cottage carrying the large leather bag—a step very different from the one she used going to the *bodega* or *carneceria*. They spoke too of how she had cared for these children when their mothers were too ill for feeding; how she would bring them into her own crowded cottage for weeks, sometimes months, until it was all right for them to be taken again to their homes. Many of these children had names the same as those of her own family. And many of the births, especially the easier ones, were like hers. So now, after the children were all grown and had families of their own, she found it difficult to think of them as being young. If she did, then they flowed one into the other, even looked alike, and she tended to confuse and forget.

Of course it had not always been like that, especially when she was still performing her duties as midwife. But there had come a year when she had what she called a Realization of Age. She could even remember the day. Was it a letter, or had she been told? No, it was a letter. From Joaquinito, the youngest, named for his father with the *ito* added to show that he was little Joaquin. He had written from America, saying he had had a son and was calling him Otto, for a German friend.

She remembered reading the letter carefully, studying and pondering over each phrase, then setting it down on the table in the kitchen. She had walked into the long narrow garden in the back that was filled with flowers, where Joaquinito once planted some avocado trees and a banana plant. It was summer then, too, and the flowers had given a numb narcotic flavor to the air (strange that she should recall that; how many times had she gone into the garden and never given a thought to the flower smell?). She had sat on the white iron bench by the avocados and stared at the roof that needed thatching again; had let the cat rub lazily under her hand, hanging limply over the edge of the bench. Joaquinito in America. A man now. With a son called Otto— such an odd name, she had never heard it before. Had all of this really happened? So many children, so many years of work. She had never found time to think. How old was he now? Twenty, Thirty? He was born when? 1912? No, it was 1913, the year of the fire in the cane fields. Then he was in his middle twenties the year of the Realization. And she was in her seventies. Raul, the oldest, had a son whose age was two years greater than Joaquinito's. A grandson older than a son.

She had walked back through the house and stood at the front door, beyond which some children were watching a tarantula shuffle across the dusty road. From where she stood, she could see her reflection in the mirror which was kept on the cage to amuse the parrot. Soon, her husband would begin to call her Abuela, grandmother, as did the children. Then, she would call him Abuelo. She had smiled a little. So this was life. Otto. She said the name again and again to herself. Joaquinito has a son. The son is called Otto.

II

1930

When Joaquinito had begun his seventeenth year, he was considered a man. Before that time, he had played with the children in the dusty streets, watched the harvesters with their machetes in the fields, and been thoroughly absorbed (in the business of growing up). He had had one job, that of running errands for old Aguilar, the keeper of the *bodega*, and it had lasted most of 1929.

At the *bodega*, he had been able to sit and listen to the men who came to drink Hatuey in the afternoons and play *cubilete* with the dice. They had many different ideas which often caused them to raise their voices or argue. In the beginning, the boy had listened silently and understood little.

But by the end of the year, he was beginning to make sense of their arguments and he felt in his heart a need to speak out and agree with those of them who said what he thought was true. There was constant talking about Machado, for instance, who had grown much harder in his second four years and was beginning to be bad for Cuba. Joaquinito wanted to help talk against this president, because he had heard his father read letters from other brothers who were in Havana and Oriente.

But the talk that had stirred him most was the talk about the mill. Only the previous year, there had come from the capital a young man called José Cuervas. He brought with him many books and leaflets, and spoke words that Joaquinito found hard to understand. But he also spoke simply, about the homes that were owned by the factory, and not by the people who passed their lives within their narrow walls. He spoke of the pay received by the farmers who grew and harvested the cane; and the long hours that kept the mill hands almost entirely from the sight of their children. And he asked them questions: He took the old men aside and asked them about the others who could never come to the *bodega* and drink Hatuey in the afternoons because the factory ignored age, and they had not raised families to support them now. He asked them, too, how many people were owned by the mill until they died.

It took most of the men in Jatibo a long time to listen to this José Cuervas from the city. They were or had been mill hands, and their resignation and patience was aided by the ignorance of an alternative to their fate. Yet Joaquinito had listened almost immediately. He hated the mill and felt he'd been storing in his heart all of the things this man said. It gave him pain to see his father, stooped now with age, hobbling off over the dusty road each morning with his tools in the oilskin bag. And he was beginning to hate his oldest brother, Raul, who had gone to live on the manager's land near the far side of town, and refused entirely to come and visit his mother or help her in any way.

But his desire to hear more of the plans of José Cuervas

was cut short when he was seventeen and it was decided that he should go to work in the sugar mill as a lathe hand under his brother Raul, who was then head foreman. His father told him he was a man now, and too old to run errands at the *bodega*. Besides, with Raul, there would be the chance of advancement. Yet Joaquinito could not suppress a slight wave of nausea as he rose with his father that first Saturday morning and began the walk through the cane fields. The mill stood at the junction of all the harvesting roads that lead from the fields, and to Joaquinito, its stacks rose black and hideous from the ground, defying the very earth on which they stood, belching their foul odor into the sky. Although born in the town, he still was nauseated whenever the wind blew from the direction of the mill and he found it hard to understand how many of the workers seemed to ignore the smell.

Still, since he was given his own machine and left entirely to himself, he enjoyed the work he did at the lathe. And he took more than passing pride in each piece he completed. He would stand back, looking at the newly turned metal, and think, There now, how is that? I have made a thing you can stand and look at or hold in your hands. Then he would put it in the tray beneath the lathe and turn to his next blueprint.

But with time, his enjoyment waned. He found that whenever he knew of a way to improve on the blueprint and produce a piece of work which was better for the job, his brother Raul would not permit him to go ahead. Then later, in a manner he could not understand, the improvements would find their way into the production. Someone else, he gathered, must see things as he did. On one occasion, he received plans for a tapered piece, thirty or forty of which would be inserted in a new rolling mechanism. His job was to put the taper on the piece, and in another section of the shop, it would be drilled. But Joaquinito's knowledge, unlike his pride, went beyond his function at one machine, and he always had a conception of the assembled product. So he brought the plans to Raul and asked how would it be if instead of drilling the piece, it was held in the head stock of the lathe and reamed.

Raul studied the plan and handed it back to his brother. "The plan calls for drilling," he said.

"I know, but if you think of assembling it in the next stage . . ."

"The next stage," said Raul, "is none of your concern. Are you the engineer?"

Joaquinito looked at him and did not answer.

"Are you?" repeated his brother.

"No."

"Then do your own work and don't worry about plans."

"But if the reaming idea is good . . ."

"If the idea was good, the engineer would know it. The engineer is an educated man."

The following week, all the tapered pieces were rerouted to another worker's lathe for production, and the new plans called for reaming. Joaquinito did not find it so hard to understand this time, and on the day of his brother's promotion to assistant engineer, he left his job at the mill and went to visit Manuel, who was then a clerk for Bacardi in Havana.

Manuel was understanding. He told his young brother that Raul had been that way for many years, that even in the games of their boyhood, he had done similar things. It was not something that came from his home, but from a quality in himself. Early in life, he determined he was better than the other workers in the mill, and he decided to advance his position. But he had neither the education nor the patience to learn, so he built himself on the qualifications of others. And once he realized the chance of being what he wanted, he pretended that his background, his parents, did not exist. That was why he, Manuel, and many of the others, no longer had anything to do with Raul. If they saw him, they were afraid of what their anger might cause.

In a way, Joaquinito knew part of this because he had heard other brothers speaking about it to his mother a few years before. But she had denied it and said to trust in God, that Raul had been a good child and it couldn't be too long before he came to visit her again. It was just that he was so busy with responsibilities.

Now, Joaquinito knew a different kind of truth and he was hurt by it. His new feeling mixed with the revulsion he had nursed for the entire mill, and the things he had heard from José Cuervas. And for some reason, Manuel's analysis annoyed him. He spent most of his time walking from one section of the city to another, and trying to understand what things, life, were all about. He had never been away from Jatibo, and Havana hypnotized him. The width of the streets, the height and color of the houses, the different food, the thorough magnificence of the capitol building, all assaulted his senses, and he walked here and there in a daze. So much was in a spin.

The day before he left for home, an incident occurred which changed his way of life. He had just passed into the section of the city known as Old Havana when he noticed a large crowd moving noisily along the street ahead of him, most of them soldiers. The civilians were jeering angrily, and the soldiers had their guns drawn. In the center of the crowd was a man being pulled along by two sergeants, and screaming at the crowd to understand what he said.

"It is the only hope," he yelled. "If you believe in Cuba . . . only with the masses . . ."

As the man passed in front of Joaquinito, he broke free from the soldiers and ran to the boy, holding him by the shoulders and looking into his face. Joaquinito thought his eyes had the look of madness in them, but he was not afraid.

"In the youth of Cuba," the man screamed, "for them and for their sons . . ."

A lieutenant stepped behind him and drove him to the ground with a blow from the butt of his gun. Not quite knowing why, Joaquinito moved toward the lieutenant with a curse and his arm raised, but was slapped across the face by a sergeant and staggered back against the crowd. The soldiers moved off down the street, with the man screaming in their midst. As Joaquinito turned to follow them, he noticed a great many leaflets lying on the ground. He bent and picked up two of them. They were the same as the ones José Cuervas had showed him in Jatibo.

"Hey!" (It was the voice of the sergeant.) "Put down that communist filth."

Joaquinito backed away from him, holding the leaflets in his hand, then glanced about. There was an alley to his left. He waved the pamphlets in the air, called out "Ha!" and ran down the alley, cleared a fence, and broke free into the street beyond, running steadily until he felt free.

III

1931

Old Laudelina, Abuela, was at last becoming content and beginning her days of rest. There was time to tend the garden, teach Consuela the duties of midwife, and watch the lives of others go by. She spoke often of how fortunate they were, how lucky the family had been. Didn't they all have jobs? Was not their name respected? And look at the fine way they kept the cottage. Crowded, yes, but never so bad as it had been when the children were all growing up.

Raul was her favorite example of how they had gotten along. He had just become chief engineer of the mill without ever having gone to school, and was probably the only man on the island to have done that. Why, even now, he was looking at property in Varadero in preparation for a summer home. And his family promised to be as large as her own. He had a son of twenty studying in the United States, and four other children in the school of the next town. She was very proud. She wished, of course, that he would come and see her, if only for an afternoon's visit, but that was probably because he was so busy. The position of chief engineer took a great deal of time. And there were social obligations. He would come someday.

Joaquinito, on the other hand, caused her to worry. He was a good son, always giving her most of the money he made, and taking care of all the household affairs. But he was uneasy. Since leaving his job as lathe hand at the mill —a good position, with promise—he had talked incessantly of the mill owners and how they were bleeding the workers. He had been spending every possible moment with some stranger named Cuervas, who hung around the *bodega.* And he was always trying to convince Consuela and herself that the town could be a better place: the streets could be paved and the roofs done in wood and tile, instead of the thatch that harbored every breed of insect; there could be spraying to stop the yellow fever and malaria. Schools could be built and, more important, the mill could make provision for the workers owning their own homes. He would spend hours talking to them of men they had never heard, men with German and Russian names whose books had put these ideas in his head. Of course it made a kind of sense that since they were part of the town, the town should be a good place in which to live. But the mill owned the town, so what was one to do? Joaquinito said he knew of a couple of things, and when he said that, the look in his eyes frightened the old woman. She wanted no trouble. If God thought the town should belong to the people, he would see that it did. After all, a great many people had lived and died there in peace.

But peace was not what the boy called it. To him, it was a desperate resignation—the beginning of apathy. And his brother, who had left this state of resignation and was in a position to do something, chose not to help those he had left behind, but to build a career upon their backs. His was the worst sin. He had married the daughter of the chief engineer before him (an aristocratic family, only vaguely aware of Raul's background and making every attempt to erase it), taken the largest house on the far side of town where the paved road went by, and held not the slightest promise for even the woman who had given him life. His absolute failure to so much as recognize his mother's saint day made him the object of Joaquinito's bitter contempt and hatred.

On one occasion, his wife had passed Joaquinito on the street where the boy had called a public meeting. There were some twenty or thirty men gathered, listening to him not three hundred yards from the house of his brother, the chief engineer. She stopped for a moment when she recognized him, then turned on her heel and walked off.

"Hola!" he had called out. But she continued walking. Joaquinito cupped his hands over his mouth and yelled after her.

"There," he yelled, "is the extreme! How many skins in Jatibo are as smooth as that one's?"

She hurried on, listening, but without turning around.

"Does the smell of sweat offend her nose? Her *nose?*" he screamed. "Her noble, aristocratic *nose?*"

The workers broke into scattered laughter, one or two of them made noises with their tongues between their lips, then they all shouted after her with catcalls and jeers. The following day, a notice appeared on the bulletin board of the mill, announcing that anyone found consorting with the brother of the chief engineer would do well to look for work in another town.

Abuela suffered greatly. It was bad enough that her sons hated each other, but to have them enemies in public and bring disgrace to the family name brought her to the edge of despair. She spoke to her husband, Joaquin, but he could offer little advice. He watched her looking at the road beyond the house and only repeated things that were true, but did not help.

"Sooner or later," he told her, "this kind of trouble had to come. Are you listening?"

She moaned a kind of yes.

"I'm sorry too about my sons. But if it must be this way, then it must. There is nothing to do; it was bound to come. People have their own minds."

A year and a half from the time he had seen the man arrested in Havana, Joaquinito, with José Cuervas and a third man from a mill town in Camaguey, organized a strike in Jatibo.

It had taken almost a year to be sure of a sufficient number of workers to risk a walkout. Cuervas had learned that ideology was not the most efficient approach, and had had Joaquinito talk to them about their homes and families instead. To those he felt would understand, Cuervas read from the leaflets. Sometimes he gave them away. And finally, enough workers had secretly defied Raul's notice to make the risk worthwhile. If they waited any longer, it would not be safe. Cuervas had already spent too much time in the town. Their position was especially helped by a foreman who had been told of Karl Marx in 1919, and was now ashamed of his position.

A strike. Joaquinito was almost delirious with joy and apprehension. He and two other men were actually leading a strike in this, his hometown. How did it all happen? Would it work? What if the army came? No matter, once it was done, then the next one would be easier. And the one after that. The workers, for this day at least, would have things in their own hands. Without having had anything to drink, Joaquinito felt drunk.

Raul's wife, however, was more than sober. And she was far too clever a woman to let pass the sublime insult she had publicly received at the hands of her brother-in-law. She had gone home after that little demonstration and fumed for hours. She had even looked in the mirror and discovered that her nose *was* rather prominent. The fact had passed out of her brain at the time of her marriage, and its sudden resurrection added immensely to her fury. She had advised one of her servants that he would do well to have his relatives in the mill inform her of Joaquinito's day-to-day activities if he wanted to see those relatives improve their position. And by tipping him well, she had learned of the strike a full week before the Saturday morning of its scheduled occurrence. She passed the news, deliciously, to her husband.

On the Saturday morning of the strike, it was raining.

The rain had come just before dawn and fell without warning. It was the worst kind of downpour, the water falling not in sheets of wind or sporadically, but in steady drenching torrents. With an old umbrella, Joaquinito walked to the *bodega*, where he found Cuervas and the other man, whose name was Fernandez. The boy was nervous and his stomach rolled and heaved incessantly. He could not join the other men in their brandies, and he was silent until the rain stopped some five minutes before they were scheduled to leave.

"Did the foreman come to see you?" he asked.

"Which foreman?" said Fernandez.

"Motrado. The one who's helping."

"He told us the chief engineer and the other foremen are not in the mill."

"Doesn't that seem odd to you?"

"You're afraid they know?"

"What else?"

"Even if they do," said Cuervas, "it's Saturday morning now." He smiled, finished his brandy, and stood. Then they all got up and walked across the muddy square in the direction of the mill.

When Motrado, the foreman, saw them coming, he went directly to the turbine room. He worked rapidly, cutting the supply of fuel to each of the gasoline engines that turned a generator. Banks of machines changed pitch, slowed down, then stopped altogether. The mill was silent.

In the town, the people who knew the pounding drone as part of their everyday lives stopped moving and looked in the direction of the strange sound of silence. And in the house of the chief engineer, the shutdown of the engines was a signal for the lieutenant in the *Guardia Rural* to call the four trucks of soldiers waiting at the edge of town.

Joaquinito, Cuervas, and Fernandez were now at the entrance to the mill. They smiled at each other, then entered side by side, and a cheer went up from about a third of the workers. The others just looked on. Cuervas walked up a flight of metal stairs leading to a tool cage, and stopped at the top to talk. His words rang out clearly, each one weighted with belief and emotion.

". . . for Cuba," he was saying. "So that your children can walk with their heads high, breathing the air of freedom . . ."

Joaquinito walked to each of the men he knew and gave them a small Cuban flag with a safety pin. Then men were confused as to where to put them, some pinning them to their shirt sleeves, while others used front pockets or even collars. Walking from man to man, the boy hardly heard a complete sentence of the speech. But he felt the excitement in the air and patted a back here, a shoulder there. The spirit, he felt, was catching on.

". . . accept the treatment they give us? Are we so much dust in the road?"

The foreman and a few others had joined Cuervas on the steps and they were all looking out over the mill. Many of the workers were beginning to gather at the bottom of the stairs, and Joaquinito's excitement mounted as he heard the low rumbling sound of anxious voices behind him, near the main entrance to the mill.

". . . to break the backs of labor . . . to eat the hand that feeds their fat, already full faces . . ."

But suddenly, he felt that something was wrong. The noise behind him grew in volume and threatened to smother the voice of Cuervas. There was a sudden cry of pain followed by a gunshot; then everything fell to pieces.

"Guardia!" someone screamed. *"Guardia Rural!"*

About fifty men moved at the entrance, but a burst of machine-gun fire stopped them, and Joaquinito saw four or five figures topple forward. His bowels became weak, and he turned and screamed at Cuervas.

"The other entrance—near the turbine room . . ."

Another series of shots echoed through the mill and Cuervas stiffened, then fell forward on the stairs. Everywhere there were screams and curses being shouted as men struggled against each other in an effort to reach the rear exit. Behind him, the sudden cries of pain continued, and

Joaquinito felt sick because he knew the *Guardia* were using their bayonets. He was one of the first to reach the
door and help pull back the large bolt; men fell over each
other trying to get out, then recoiled as the sound of gun-
fire changed direction and the first workers out the door
slumped to the muddy ground. Joaquinito's eyes were
blinded with tears and he could not stop the stream of
curses that flowed from between his clenched teeth. He
picked up a screwdriver to attack the first soldier close to
him, but he was in the middle of the crowd and could not
get free. In a few moments, the voices of the soldiers rose
above the other sounds, the crowd noise subsided; then,
almost at once, only the orders of the officers could be
heard. Next to a lieutenant, Joaquinito could see his brother
standing, holding a rifle. The boy pushed his way through
the crowd, but stopped when he came to the body of
Cuervas, shot in the chest and face. His legs went weak
beneath him and he dropped on his knees next to the body.
He felt as if he should hold or touch it, but was not able
to. He knelt quietly for a few moments, the tears running
down his cheeks; and when he stood, his brother Raul, the
chief engineer, was standing in front of him.

"Hello, Communist," he said.

Joaquinito looked at him, but was silent.

"What happened?" asked Raul slowly. "What happened
to your strike?"

The boy wanted to speak out, but his teeth were locked
together.

"You can't talk now? You could talk before . . . Talk,
Communist!"

Joaquinito's lips parted slightly and he was just about
to speak to his brother, to use on him the vilest curse a
man of Spanish blood could speak, when Raul swung the
butt of the gun up from the ground, catching him in the
groin. He made a short gurgling sound in his throat and
dropped to the floor before the flat part of the stock caught
him full in the face, and knocked him over on his back. He
coughed and spit blood, but failed to yell.

The following week, he and Fernandez were indicted and tried, and were each given twenty years at hard labor. Five miles from the town of the prison, the truck carrying the prisoners was intercepted, the soldiers killed, and both men were in Miami before the month was out. All of this took place during the second term of Machado y Morales' reign, and the year before a sergeant by the name of Batista led the enlisted men in a revolution that began a cycle much like the one which was ending.

IV

1942

Eleven years had passed. Another decade, a new generation. The Second World War had begun.

But Abuela could not remove the needle of loss from her heart. Since the departure of her youngest son, she behaved as though she were in mourning. She watched absently as old Joaquin got up from the bed each day, dressed himself painfully, and shuffled off to the mill. He was determined to work until his death. She listened as Consuela spoke of this or that birth, and how the new mothers had taken the delivery. She tended the garden, giving special care to the large banana tree and avocados, accepted visitors, even smiled occasionally at the aging parrot. But she could not remove from her heart the aching pain of loss. Joaquinito had been her favorite and was gone.

He wrote now and again, telling of America and New York, giving news of his wife and son. But when she answered and begged him to return, if only for a short visit, his reply was always no, there was only one thing that could make him return, and the time had not yet come. Besides, he said, he was always needed at the shop because of the war. And each reply renewed the edge of the blade in her breast.

Raul, of course, had gone on to great things. He had

made a fortune in the sugar business, and at the age of fifty-five was ready to retire. His oldest son, Herrido, was chief engineer of the mill in Colon at thirty-one, and had already put up a house next to his father's in Varadero. Some of the mills were becoming unionized, but with the coming of age, his success behind him, and a year-round life at the sea about to begin, Raul cared little. Herrido, educated at the University of Michigan, cared less.

This was the state of affairs when old Joaquin, wearied with a hard life at the mill and unable to console his wife, fell dead in the dusty street before the cottage while watching some children wrestling in the dirt.

If Abuela was distracted before the death of her husband, she was now committed to the depths of despair. Sleep was impossible and she spent her days sitting alone in the house, refusing to see anyone but her immediate family, accepting from them nothing but their part in the grief. Raul sent a card, but said he was unable to make the trip from Havana, where he was on business.

Occasionally, the old woman would grip the sides of her chair, attempt to rise, and make little sounds of exasperation in her throat. Consuela, who stayed with her now, knew she could not last long since she had abandoned food almost completely. The cataracts, threatening for years, had now almost covered her eyes. The doctor said her only hope was rest, and he suggested that if she got away from the house for a short while, maybe to the sea, she might have a year, perhaps two. Still, Consuela knew that it was the torment of her mother's mind that caused the failing, and that to move her from the house she had never left might bring on the end much sooner. But when she awoke on a number of occasions to find Abuela sitting straight up in bed, looking at the wall, and holding a conversation with her dead husband, Consuela called Raul at Varadero and begged him to make room for her there so at least part of the family could be together at the death.

After talking with Elena, Raul finally decided to arrange accommodations for both his mother and Consuela at the hotel, since his wife would not hear of the woman dying in her home.

Abuela, almost every conviction abandoned, allowed herself to be taken to the three-car train in the next town, and from there to Varadero, where she was surprised to find not only Raul, but Manuel, Cecelia, and Humberto as well. Consuela had written to each of them, and they arranged to stay at the hotel. She had also sent a long telegram to Joaquinito.

In the excitement of the reunion, and anticipating the arrival of her youngest son—for she knew full well that this was the one reason he had written of, the only cause for his return—Abuela fell and struck her head. She was almost eighty. All was lost.

She had been lying quietly for what seemed like a very long time, half aware of the numb chill taking hold of her body, when she sensed Consuela's voice at the edge of her consciousness. The voice spoke of Joaquinito. It said he was on his way to Cuba. He would be there soon. Soon . . . But she could not meet him like this, lying still with death hovering somewhere in the room. He had last seen her from the back of the truck that was taking him off to prison: she had stood there with her husband and kept her head high until he was out of sight. To be lying this way was defeat, the way of an old woman. And what if he brought his family? Such a way to meet the people she had never seen. Here now, she would show them.

Throughout most of the night she fought the numbness in her limbs and refused to admit the death feeling, talking to it at times, defying it or treating it with reproach. In the morning, she told Consuela she was better and wished to sit on the porch of the hotel and wait for her son.

She rocked slowly, looking at the sea, but with the thick film over her eyes she could make out little more than a many-colored haze. The haze was pale green where the beach ended and the sea began; then it changed softly to aqua, then to blue, and deeper blue, until in the distance, there was no way of knowing where the sky began. The sky could have been the entire vista, beginning some thirty yards from the hotel and stretching to infinity with no sea at all. It was a queer feeling and her eyes were filled, almost bursting, with the glory of these sun-brushed colors she had never known quite the same way. She thought of Jatibo, the town where she had passed all her days—it was just a small farm when she knew it first, no mill, no cane— but now it seemed so far away. She should miss it. She should want to return. But when she had allowed herself to be taken from the house, when she had crossed the threshold and walked out to the strange taxi waiting on the dusty street, an unknown driver, she had not been able to look back. The garden, the parrot, her husband's chair, all the little statues and religious objects—they seemed the possessions of another person. They were not hers any more. There was a woman called Laudelina, whose house that was; a young woman who talked with her husband who had just taken the blacksmith's job at the mill. A good job, too, with promise. And sitting alone on the rocking chair at Varadero, she knew that the house no longer wanted her. She would even be a stranger to the town.

How odd these thoughts were. She rocked and waited, the numb chill hovering near her, waiting to take hold as soon as she allowed it. There was some movement to her left, some people coming toward her . . . who were they? "Consuela?" she asked.

One of the figures moved to her side, awkwardly. The shape was clouded, but still she knew him. It was Joaquinito when he was younger—when he used to play in the road outside their house. But no, it was someone else. Who then? "Do you know your grandson?" asked Consuela.

The old woman stopped rocking and leaned forward. Her grandson? Could this be . . . but what was his name? Ah, how could she forget, she had just been thinking of it. She held out her arms and the boy came to her and said something in English. Tears welled in her eyes and she clasped her arms around his back.

"Strong," she said, "and tall . . ."

The chill moved toward her, but she shrugged it back. There was another shape now, larger this time, a man. He was standing behind the boy, his body almost filling her many-colored sky. She looked, blinked the tears back, and looked again.

Joaquinito walked forward and knelt by the chair, holding his mother around the waist. She held him the same way she had held his son, and rocked slowly in the chair, her head back, looking at the sky, her heart filled with the anguish of love. And she said his name over and over in half-audible tones.

That night, she fell asleep content and gave no thought to fighting death. Raul left for his home in Jatibo because his wife would not stay another moment in Varadero and he was uneasy in his brother's silent presence.

At three-thirty in the morning, the old woman awoke with a cry of pain and the family gathered very quickly in her bedroom. She asked for Joaquinito to hold her, then she talked freely, incoherently, to everyone present. Was Raul, the oldest, there? Joaquinito answered yes. At one point she looked at a place where no one was standing, and talked with her dead husband. She used the same tone and inflection as she had been using with her children. "He wants me with him," she explained. She looked around the room again and seemed satisfied. The youngest and the oldest were there. Then she allowed the chill to invade and rattle in her chest, and she died.

By morning, Joaquinito had sent most of the telegrams and made arrangements for the funeral. By four o'clock that afternoon, he had had the body moved to the house of his oldest brother, Raul, and the rooms there were filling rapidly with relatives and friends. He hung a wreath of black leaves on Raul's front door, another on Herrido's. Because it was summer, they buried Abuela on the following day.

Almost immediately after the burial, Joaquinito left his son, Otto, in care of Consuela, and drove to Jatibo. Beside him in the front seat was still another wreath and a small

box tied with string. He was going to the house of his
brother, the chief engineer.

The ride took almost two hours on the Central Highway.
It was dinnertime when he arrived, and not yet dark. When
he opened the door of the car in his brother's driveway,
Joaquinito heard the sound of the mill for the first time in
almost twelve years. He stopped for a moment and looked
in the direction of the roar. Even now, there was an ugli-
ness to the structure, a feeling that it did more than object
to the people that swarmed through its middle. It defied
them as it did the earth upon which it stood.

He turned and walked up the steps to the front door and
hung a wreath on the knocker. Then, with the small box
under his arm and without ringing the bell, he went into
the house and followed the sound of voices until he came
to the dining room. As he entered, every sound stopped.
There was no tinkle of glass or silver, no voice or whisper.
Only the drugged pulse of the mill as it came through the
walls and windows, muted now, almost soft. There were
seven people at the table: Raul, Elena, Herrido, and four
other children. They had just finished their soup and there
were large plates of yellow rice on the table, with here and
there a casserole of chicken, pieces of pork, and black
beans. Joaquinito walked to the middle of the long table
and broke the string on the box. Then he turned it over,
spilling out a pile of dry sandy dirt on the white tablecloth.
No one made a sound.

"Some earth, Raul," he said slowly. "From the grave of
your mother."

He stood still for a moment, looking at his oldest brother,
then turned and left the house. As soon as he closed the
door behind him, he wept. He drove the car across the
town and stopped again in front of a cottage that sat with
three or four others at the edge of a dusty road. And he
removed his hat before going in to look for the last time
at the house of his birth.

BIRTHDAY

A fragment

I like this. This is his whole "party" mind again. I surprised him one time with a birthday party, and I've never seen a grown person look so little and so delighted. He came in and there were decorations all over and balloons and people sitting around and glasses tinkling and music and all party things that he liked. He had no idea any of it was going to happen, and he walked in and his jaw dropped . . . And for a second he looked wide-eyed, lost. But then he joined in laughing, talking, and being the center of attention—as if he'd been there all along.

M.F.

When the second hand's soft sweep tells me
That the year before has gone and now
I stand grown older: I lie and cry
For the bright white cake with candles I used to see;
And for the children, chattering bubbles in a Babel,
Who would crowd about me with popping toys
Of rainbow and pink paper of crepe that stretched;
And for curls of girls reciting and the jealous-eyed boys
Who brought presents in ribbons of red
And fed themselves with chocolate babies.

TWO
IRISH STORIES

Dick loved Ireland. He loved to tell stories about it too, about all his Irish relatives; he had great Irish and/or Cuban relative stories.

A lot of his spirit was Irish; he loved singing in bars and getting drunk—and telling ghost stories. He could frighten his Irish mother with a ghostly tale.

Dick went off to war in Ireland to be romantic; he really wanted to live all the things he wrote about and all the things that he felt. It was luck that they deported him when he was eighteen. But to have a dream about something and go off and do it, that's a great thing—even if it's as lousy as going off to war . . .

M.F.

With a Copy of Dylan under My Arm

Three weeks of bread, raw eggs, eels and newly dug potatoes in the flax and hay dappled country of Lough Neagh had eaten their consuming way into my body, softened by cities. The red-faced girls with their passive bodies, the black-toothed farmers with swollen hands, the twisted fishermen with tilted caps, the hardened women with their shawls—all had twisted their worming selves into my soul, weakened by wandering. Too young to taste the sweetness, too restless to see the beauty, too full of lust to want to stay—I mounted a monster of a bus and with a small leather bag that had stickers, and a copy of Dylan under my arm, I rolled and tumbled, an inert sack of a boy, towards buildings of brick and windows of wine- and sin-filled women waiting in black silks for the bus that bore me to them all.

Eighteen and six for the fare to Belfast and the conductor knew I was American. I must buy dark clothes and thickened tweeds, I thought. I must buy green checkered shirts and wide-bottomed trousers and make frowns to look troubled and pensive. I must smoke Players and Will's Woodbines and drink tea and stout and Tennents and wear large sweaters and only look American when some woman, not caring for her husband sitting in a stupor at the pub with darts, would look for someone new and foreign to carry her away to the sea and love on the sand. Eighteen and six for the fare to Belfast and the rocking, lurching, throbbing bus beat me slowly into sleep.

I woke in Antrim, angry with me for not seeing who had boarded and left the bus. There had been a factory girl who got on at Randelstown and who sat beside me when she saw my black hair. She would be twenty-seven and have wistful eyes. She would look at me with longing and hope that I would waken to talk to her; and she would breathe softly and warm into my ear and we would catch the steamer from Belfast and take a cabin with dark heavy wood and three portholes and a bed. We would see the shops of Heysham in the morning and I would pat her chin and wink at her and then take the boat train to London, leaving her on the platform crying and torn between her factory and suicide.

Antrim was a lovely town with white-washed houses and large oak pubs. The sun was shuffling slowly back and forth between black bunches of clouds that hung heavy and low over the afternoon land and I waited for the bus to lurch forward again that I might sleep. And wake in Belfast and go to a small pub with pewter and brass hanging on the walls.

I woke again on the long long hill that turns its slightly sloping way into the beat of the city. Down past Aldergrove Aerodrome with the vampire jets waiting for blood. Down past the Falls Road with the rebels waiting for British. Down, down, to the gentle pulsing of the buildings where the terminal was grey and dirty and bristling uniforms hurried about carrying pads and packages and pushing carts with papers.

"Which way to the city center?" I asked of a blue and silver uniform with a strip of gold on his cap.

He answered with turns left and right and two blocks this way and three blocks that so I ignored his voice and thanked him before I turned to follow the people walking past the bargain windows and teas for one and three.

I walked past theatres and Cooks and bombed-out post office, stores with trench coats and cravats and driving gloves, and slowly—painfully—I remembered the city I had known somewhere in the nightmare past. The City Hall would be at Donegal Square. Long and complex with proud domes thrust up, it would be sitting sadly and thinking of the years it had known. Poor dark building, you must have a poem someday.

And now I walked on quickly for here and there were things I knew and longed to touch again. I walked down one long narrow street with tiny sidewalks and buildings that had no steps. I listened to my feet make noise. Then I turned and snuck back into the seethe of the city at the time when the shops close. Around I turned and went, not knowing where, until my legs grew tired and I could find no faces from the past so I looked for my pub with pewter.

Pardon me, but could you tell me where I might find a pub with pewter?

But I could not bring myself to ask unless I found my maiden with the wistful eyes so I went to the first place I saw and had four stouts and felt that it was not such a bad pub after all. Away the eels and the kiss of the lough on the land. And a few more stouts, you keeper of the bar. Away the red-faced Marys and drunken Hughies. Away all you shades that are now fifty and now ten million miles away. And as I asked for just one more, I found myself, a small round myself, in the mirror gazing intently at myself, and next to me was a brightened eye in a whitened head.

"Hello old sage."

"How are y' lad?"

And soon we sang *The Minstrel Boy* and he cried for Erin and I cried for me. He was one of the Falls Road Boys and he wanted to blow up the Queen.

"There is a plan . . ." he'd begin before we'd sing. And cry. His friends came in and someone told a joke about newlyweds and Nelson's pillar so we all roared with reddened eyes for fifteen minutes. Someone said I wasn't much of a Yankee to be singing with all the boys and my face grew red with pride as I bought them all a stout.

And now let's sing *The Ram,* boys, or any song that's good for a crack. This is a group that's good for a crack so we'll have a few more but nobody vomit to spoil it.

"And if y'r Orange," said the old brightened head, "y'r welcome among us if y' give us a bit of a crack." And the old songs twisted through the smell of smoke and men and malt brown air.

The rolling pitching of the floor brought my mind to my kidneys so I forced myself, a lumpy wart-hog, here and there about the pub until I found the bathroom. I saw myself in the mirror again and sank to the tiles in a convulsion of laughter. *But listen*—there is laughter beyond the door. There is singing and sport and good crack beyond the door. Then through the door to reach it all; beyond the door to reach it all; always a door to reach it all. Back I went and sat and gurgled noises with my stout as I laughed and cried. And Cried. *Good-night good men,* I cried.

I crashed and tumbled out of the pub and sprawled, a spreading piece of jam, into the night.

"To a bed," I told the pitted-faced tobacco-toothed driver, "with a blond and bouncing prostitute in black silk sheets."

He took me to a small hotel with pastel pillars and an old bone woman for a night clerk.

"Do you have," I blurted as I bumped through the door to my room, "a blond and bouncing prostitute?"

She looked at me with mothered wrinkle and moved me to my large deserted white-sheeted cold and lonely bed. And my pillow held my head as I slept the empty night away.

It should have been raining softly and dark the next morning but the sun was flung down brightly on the streets of stone and I woke up clothed and feeling tarred beneath a giant of a quilt with feathers. I rose all wrinkled and with a throat of burning sand and I searched the halls for a bathroom.

Outside, in the cruel glare of the day, I fit myself back into the afternoon city and looked for a place to ease my roaring pit of stomach. I bought the *Telegraph* to hold beneath my arm and I walked swiftly, looking occupied and belonging, to a large café on Lombard Street with wooden stalls and high windows. I tossed away the unread paper and looked for the table with the nicest waitress but I saw none at all so I sat next to the window where I could drink tea and watch the high-headed men with long black suits and twigs of umbrellas float by in the street outside.

"Have you ordered, luv?" she asked.

"No I haven't but I'll have the one-and-six tea."

And as she bobbed away, a light and happy wisp of
flame, I felt myself grow warm. She came back with tray
of tea and toast and biscuits and jam. But I only saw her
wistful eyes. Large and violet and almost oriental. She set
down the tray with long white hands of powder and when
she poured my tea, she looked at me and smiled a smile.

"American, aren't you?" she half whispered and I knew
she must be mine. By nine we would be two passioned
forms loving in the largest bed in Belfast intrigued and in
love with our touches and sighs.

"Yes. Quite. And you might be Irish, might you not?"
I whispered back.

"I might," she said and her laughing eyes burned me
down to a charred black heap of ash and she wandered
back past the brown wooden stalls and she knew my eyes
followed and wanted. I drank my tea slowly—so slowly—
and waited for her to come back and smile and laugh with
her eyes. Her skin would be so fresh and cool. But she
stayed away until I finished and then she came back with
the check.

"Like your tea, luv?"

"Yes thank you. It was quite good."

"Leaving, luv?"

"Yes—I suppose so."

"Cheerio then, luv."

"Well—good-by."

"Good-by, luv."

And away she bobbed again, leaving me to walk out
stunned and lonely and with thoughts and visions of a life
in an empty bed with a nightmare pillow.

I drifted back to the City Hall and sat on a bench with
an old man and pigeons. And I wrote letters telling people
the things they knew I'd tell them if I ever wrote. The
pigeons sat on the bench and the old man: flapping and
cooing, they leaped from his head to his arm and peck peck
pecked at the small seeds that he gave to them all. But they

would not sit on me. So I went to find a tiny cluttered book-store I once had known where I could read some Dylan I had missed and talk to the lovely young owner and convince her to sell my very newest book in her store. Then I'd leave her tingling and run home to write my newest book. But it was a half-day for the shops and the bookstores were all closed and there would be no very newest book. No any book.

Now I was alone to choke away my breath so I found a pub with no pewter and had a Jameson's and a Guinness with a broken man who hated war because they had made his son a sausage at Dunkirk. He made me sad so I left and walked to the Plaza dance hall and thought thoughts of things that had slipped by me in the years since gone. I could hear again the banging band and the stomping feet on the floor as the couples rose and fell like some large-geared quick-moving wood-carved Swiss plaything.

"Dance, sweetheart?" they'd ask a girl the way the Yankee pictures showed. And chewing gum, she'd nod.

But the Plaza was quiet now and its ghosts were gone so I had another Jameson's and went back to my café on Lombard Street. And down I sat, a hum in my head, and I hoped with pounding body that she would come. Come, come sweet vestal for the fire is dying and I will perish with it. Come with your Chinese violet eyes and cool long hands of white.

"Hello, luv," I heard and my being stopped.

"Good evening," I said, "I'd like some tea." And some you, I thought, I'd like some you. With your eyes and your hands. And your laugh and your walk. All mine, all mine.

And when she comes back, I'll sit, a detached bundle of intrigue with American cigarettes and green passport and when she passes I'll touch her arm and blowing smoke around her I'll ask her to come away with me.

"Could I have some water, miss, my tea is terribly strong."

"Right away, luv."

Away to some hotel by the port. Or perhaps to Brighton —then it would be like an English novel. A stone cottage

with red flowers tumbling out over the window sills and a
rainbowed flagstone path twisting to a wood and iron door
six inches thick and with a creak. And in the back there
would be the sea with coarse brown British sand and
chunks of grass here and there. And we would lie and
laugh and leave the twisted snarl of a bitter earth somewhere not there.

"Would you like something else, luv?"

"Yes. Yes I would, my violet eyes, I'd like to know your
name."

And before she answered Jean, my blood flew out and
away from my heart and surged hot to my face and I felt
my ears tingle and my eyes grow glossy.

Perhaps it was too quick and she would turn and run,
screaming for the manager. Perhaps she hated men because
her father whipped her with a rod when she was a wee girl.

"But my eyes are blue, luv," she said and I melted slowly
in my straw-backed chair.

"Your eyes are violet, Jean," I said. And your skin is soft
and cool, I thought, and mine is dark and warm.

"It's the frock that does it, luv," she said.

The frock was green with a small lace apron and I knew
I must take her away.

"Do you like being a waitress, Jean?"

"I like it fine, luv."

"Do you meet many people?"

"Oh lots, luv."

"And do they take you out at all?"

"Well some of them do, luv, but I have a boy."

He was seven feet tall and weighed nineteen stone and
worked in a quarry and crushed his enemies' heads in
massive marble blocks that he held in his huge hands. But
he could not keep her from me. It had been like this so
many times in the wild crying thoughts of my nights before
I slept. And she was here before me.

"Would you like to go out with me, Jean?"

"Where would we go, luv?"

And as her eyes betrayed her thoughts, I pounded apart

in longing and joy and said I'd meet her when she was
through.

I walked to Burtons on the corner and bought a black
beret for seven shillings from a salesman who was short and
thin with a nose bent over a fresh red moustache that sat
on sallow skin.

Jean was waiting, bright and blond, with green shoes
that had short thick heels. She saw me coming and walked
to meet me with her hands in the warm pockets of her coat.
Her eyes were still violet.

"Hello, luv," she said.

"All set?"

"If you are, luv."

"And now," I said, "you are going to take me to a pub
that looks old and has pewter."

"Kelly's Cellars?" she asked.

"If it's old and has pewter," I said and she laughed and
took my arm and we walked alone, despite the people,
down small dark bank street to Kelly's Cellars.

The windows were brown and yellow and thick so that
all you could see were turning beams of colored light. And
when we walked inside, I knew quite simply that I had
found it.

There were dark and heavily clothed men sitting in
smoke on old cushioned barrels before a bar that was only
three feet high. On the walls were plates of hammered brass
where packs of beagles were bursting through rows of
hedges followed hotly by black-booted men on horseback.
There were pots and pitchers of copper and pewter hung
between heads of deer while heavy dark beams stretched up
from the floor and reached across the ceiling. There were
stained wine casks which sat beneath cloth pictures of round
children gamboling like sheep in a vineyard.

And the barman wore suspenders and a tie with a high
collar. His sleeves were rolled to the elbow as he shuffled
from place to place, filling a flask here and pulling a stout
there.

We went past the bar to the stalls with high partitions

and we sat at a table carved with the initials of a shade I knew was still there. She had a lager and I had a Jameson's with a Guinness and we talked lightly and foolishly until I took her hand and she looked at me with a flaming smile. And we touched our legs together and I had another drink. Oh Jean sweet Jean wee Jean we will wander off together and crush ourselves away with love. No worlds or wounds or horrors will be ours. Only our bodies beating out against each other's surge of life. Forever my Jean? Ah, who could say *now*? But away will we go—and then I asked her and she put her other hand on my arm and looked down at the table and I had another drink. Oh why think my Jean, we live but once. And her mind tore and screamed and she opened her mouth and shook her head and I thought she would cry but she only held me tightly and touched her leg to mine.

"More Jameson's," I said and she looked down past my eyes and rose slowly away from me. She came to my side of the table and asked me for three-pence for the phone.

"I'll be right back, sweet," she whispered and she kissed me, the kiss of a warm wind, on the mouth.

"All right, Jean," I said and watched her walk away and I had three more drinks before I knew she was not coming back to me. So good-by wee Jean, soft beating blood. Good-by my heart of a brief night gone. Hello again to the nightmare real and I'll have another drink. And one more for a bit of a crack and maybe someone will sing *The Galway Shawl* and the old men will sit, ale in fist, looking out to nowhere as they hear the sad words and think of the days they might have had. Hello old men and welcome me, young driftwood waiting for the moon, to your pipes and caps so we may sing and laugh and roll away what is beyond the walls.

Outside, there was a slowly gathering mist and I listened to my footsteps drop as I walked through the city, quieted by night. I stopped in front of Cooks and looked at the posters of Paris and London and Bombay. Then I walked some more until I came to a wee hotel and I drank tea.

An End to
a Young Man

I

The American sat with a man called McAlear, drinking Jamesons and Guinness chasers, each of them going on at first as if nothing of particular importance was planned for the coming evening. Some light discussion of the gray Belfast architecture, the hammered brass plates and pewter mugs that hung from walls, the football pools, and then once the question of losing citizenship for serving with the organization. Through all of the talk except the last part the American had been watching the long legs of the waitress. Then he looked across the narrow, initial-carved table and said:

"It's only something printed on the passport, that citizenship nonsense. They won't bother me unless there's an incident."

"Is that it then?" asked McAlear, smiling, finishing his whiskey and following it with a long gulp of stout. Not going into the evening's business. The American waited, fingered the beads of moisture on his pint, then swallowed it and called for another round, giving his attention back to the waitress.

He had been in Kelly's Cellars before and seen this same girl gliding about the smoke-thick room where the men sat heavily on the used casks at the bar. As she returned he watched the weight of her breasts in her frock. She looked back for an instant, smiled faintly, then named the drinks as she placed them on the table.

"Two Jamesons, two pints for chasers."

"On the tab again, please," said McAlear.

The girl wiped the top of the table with a damp piece of terrycloth, darkening the wood as she worked, waiting at one point for the American to lift his hands away, then returned behind the bar, the muscles in her calves making ovals with each step. McAlear lifted his glass and said, "Steadies the nerves."

They drank again silently, and when the waitress went out of sight into one of the other rooms, the American decided to mention something about the business of the evening. It came out.

"I have to be in Toome just after dark."

"Aye, they told me that."

He waited, then tried again.

"Was there any change in plan?"

"You knew about the Antrim diversion?"

"Since last week."

"No, no changes from then. Only"—McAlear took another long drink from the stout, the dark foam catching some of his mustache—"only I thought we might have a wee chat, so to speak."

"That's all right with me," from the American, shifting his weight.

"I was concerned. About your feelings in this."

"I'm sorry, I don't understand."

"In the matter of tonight, you see. Your feelings."

Jesus, he thought. "It should be easy with the Antrim diversion."

"No, no, not about that. Since coming here you've done quite well; great optimism about your work. But privately, from my own point of view, you see, I would like knowing why you haven't asked after the purpose and function of ending Partition."

"Are they dissatisfied with me?"

"Not at all, I said you've done very well. But from my private point of view, you see, I would like knowing how you consider the severe risk of tonight, and you not Irish to begin with. Internment at Crumlin is unpleasant at the least, nor should your country be lost to you easily."

"That's just something—"

"They put on the passport; yes, you mentioned that. After the war you'll understand, a good lot of the Irish-Americans stayed on and did their discharge here, some of them working for us. It's only I remember how they did it to keep on with something, and not for Ireland at all, you might say."

"This is a hell of a time to bring that up."

"A hell of a time, yes. Yes, perhaps. Still . . ."

"I'm aware of the risks, you know. A long while before—"

"Of course, yes. You do know about all that. And there is no question there at all. I am asking about Partition. You have really been quite silent on that issue." He paused and drained his glass, speaking again when he had tipped it back empty between his mouth and the table. "It is the issue at stake. As you well know."

"I do my work."

"We know that."

"Have there been complaints from the commandant?"

"None. There's even what you might call a special affection for you at Falls Road."

"Then?"

"It was just my own wondering, so to speak. Your well-being is involved; you know so little about why we use your work."

"Is it always necessary?"

"Ah. That's as may be. Of course. Would you care for some more of that whiskey?"

"No. Thank you."

"You see on the Queensboat when she lets go tomorrow —I mean, assuming there is no difficulty this evening— On the boat there may well be five men."

The American had been tracing a figure eight on the intial-carved tabletop, using the moisture in his pint. He stopped doing this for a moment when McAlear said five men, then continued again reversing the direction of his finger. McAlear went on.

"It will still have no one aboard tonight, they sign on in the morning. But they'll be there when she lets go. You're sure about the whiskey? Does you good when the evenings be early like this."

The American attempted to go on with the figure eights but found it difficult. "I'm fine. Why don't I just finish this one and then go."

"As it suits you."

The waitress passed back through the room, hesitated a moment as McAlear waved her by, then went over behind the bar, smiling at the American as she went.

"An Phoblacht abu," said McAlear.

"The Republic," he answered, and they drank.

II

He had known about the patrol boat for some time, but only as a breed of concept, an objective thing: there was in his mind's eye a picture of the boat at anchor in the river under the Toome bridge, a sergeant of the Royal Ulster Constabulary pacing the bridge, an occasional lorry rumbling by before making the sharp right turn into the town, the boat timbers squeaking against the quayside. Two light hawsers to secure her bow and stern. Very simple, the whole thing in a frame. But in his concept he had not considered any people. Driving to the cottage in Antrim he tried to place the five men in the framed picture, but they failed to fit. Perhaps if he moved the boat. The anchor aweigh, the boat easing off the quayside, out under the bridge through the river channel, and into the lough itself. That was better. There were two of them in the wheelhouse drinking tea from a thermos, one in the bow with binoculars and two in the stern with guns. All of them with their black peaked caps, the gold-woven seal of the crown. With the boat in his mind's eye that way, the throttle just increased to running speed, rudder standard, it was easier to

fit the five men. He tried to include the bomb as well, but
that was considerably more difficult. He had no knowledge
of the engine spaces below the wheelhouse, and he could
not invent them in his head. That would have to wait. All
right, he told himself while still driving. So there are people
to worry about now. Whose concern was that?

McAlear? *Just my own wondering, so to speak.* Jesus.
Meeting him in Cork when the *Britannic* had docked and
the long ride in the car up through Dublin toward the
North. All along the route the discussion of farming and
what could be seen on the hillsides and in the valleys.

What is that gold-colored crop?

Flax. It's early here. In the North it's still a touch green.

I've never seen it before. What use does it have?

Linen. Smiling, the pipe still wedged under his gray-red
mustache. After the harvest they lay it in water holes, keep
it down with stones, you see; then dry it after the outer
stalk decays and spin it.

Spin it? After the decaying?

The fibers gain strength in the water as they die. It's
a profound crop, really.

When will they harvest in the North?

Three weeks. Maybe a month. You'll be there to see
it. Would you like to stop for a little taste? It's cocktail
hour in your country, I believe.

In your country. Always a touch of something like that.
Still, the man seemed to have an interest. Taking him
through the flax fields in the North and showing him the
harvest. The wind having beaten it down too far for scyth-
ing, he explained, the need to tear it from the ground
by hand.

It happens often, Yank. Someday maybe they'll get a
machine for it, eh?

Wouldn't any cutting machine work?

The length of stalk makes for the fiber strength. If you
cut anywhere but at the bottom, you'd lose the strength.
Would you like pulling a bit?

McAlear had shown him how to grasp a handful of the stalks close to the ground, tear them up with a quick tug, then slap them against a trousers leg to jar the loose earth at the roots. Later the American learned how to make the thumb knot with marsh rushes for binding the flax up to stalk. It was the same man who had bought him the drinks in Kelly's Cellars who had shown him all that. At the end of the day in the fields, when the women were coming out across the harvested spaces with cannisters of evening tea, singing snatches of songs as they came, and while the men were putting their shirts back on and scraping the mud from the trousers legs where the earth had collected over the hours of slapping stalks, McAlear had put one hand on his shoulder and said to him while facing the approaching women:

It has been this way for many hundreds of years.

That night the American had drunk with them in the Armagh pub, getting light-headed on stout and playing darts and singing. It was the one day when he almost forgot coming to Ireland for no other reason than because he had never seen a war and he wanted to know the feeling of it and have it in his experience.

Now he was driving back along the road from Belfast, where he had had the drink with McAlear, on his way to Antrim where he would be met by the two diversion men. In the cottage was his bomb, and thinking about it he pressed his foot down on the gas pedal and listened absently to the sound of the tires on the damp road.

III

It was dark and the American sat in the thatched cottage at a wooden table across from the two men. A tillie lamp glowed from the beam where it was suspended, and the mantle released a muffled hiss. The two men wore caps and leather jackets, they smelled from the fishing, which was their livelihood, and they were fitting fuses into a set of six grenades. The American was examining a caulked box.

"Are you sure it's watertight?"

"It was tested this morning," said one of them, who had no teeth. The other had red hair showing from under his cap.

The American ran a finger along the caulked seams of the box's interior, nodded, then lifted over the plastic explosives and secured them to the screw eyes that had been placed there. He connected the red and yellow leads to the terminals of the timing device, checked the spring knob, then wound it and placed the entire assembly on top of the explosives, filling the open spaces with rockwool. There was a bottle of whiskey and three bars of Cadbury's milk chocolate on the table, and the bottle was half empty.

"She looks a good job," said the other man.

"Thanks."

He lifted the bottle to his lips and took a drink as if it were wine. It went down much the same way with no harshness, and he felt that he could probably finish the whole bottle alone, the way it was failing to reach him.

"Have another, Yank," said the one with red hair. "The water be's cold. Touches the blood, that."

He drank again and passed the bottle, each of the men drinking small amounts in turn.

"It's eight twenty," he reminded them. They nodded and the toothless one looked up curiously.

"Do y' get much singin' where y' be in the city?"

"In Belfast?"

"Aye."

"Only now and again."

The man finished with one grenade, pulled his ear lobe, then began on another, handling it as if it were an egg. "Y've not heard a song called 'Roddy McCorley'?"

"I don't think, no, I haven't."

The Irishman nodded and opened one of the chocolate bars, breaking it in three pieces, passing the largest piece

across the table. "He's buried right there near the Queensboat. Hung on Toome bridge."

"Was he with the organization?"

"Oh, well, aye, y' might call it that. It be's near eighteen
hundred."

"Just a young cub, he was," said the other man.

"Y'll no doubt see the stone, a Gaelic cross with writing
on it. In the Irish."

"I've seen photographs," said the American, "the ones
taken of the boat."

"Aye, where they tie the Queensboat. They won't tie it
there no longer, but."

"I think they won't," said the other man, chuckling and
eating his bit of chocolate. They passed the bottle again
and finished with the grenades.

"Well," said the one with red hair, "keep an ear t' the
wind"—he patted the grenades—"and listen for these boys."

Both men stood up and strung the grenades at their
waists under the jackets. Then the toothless one hesitated
and came back across the room to stand in front of the
American.

"There be's a fence what the Crown put around the
gravestone. Y'll see it there above the landing, they keep
it locked, don't you know." He reached into the patch
pocket of his jacket and removed a pair of heavy-duty
cable cutters. "I was thinkin' that maybe if y'd have the
time—knowin' it's not planned or nothin'—but if y' have
the time at all, y' might cut that lock away." The man ad-
justed his cap and pulled his ear lobe. "It's a bloody insult
they've done, puttin' up a fence and lockin' the stone back
like that."

"Suppose the R.U.C.'s on the bridge?"

"Only if y' can, yank. We've had no chance before. It's
a disgrace and an insult, keepin' it so y' can't have a prayer
there an odd time."

"If I can," he told him, "OK." He took the cable cutters
and laid them next to the box on the table.

The two men turned at the door and smiled back at him. "Give 'em what for, yank."

"Slainte," said the toothless one.

"Luck, yourselves."

He waited for the sound of their steps to vanish before he turned and faced the table again. There was an inner tube to inflate and a garrison-weight belt to connect to the box. When he had done these things he looked at the cable cutters for a moment, then put them in his pocket and went out to the car.

He was lying in a recently harvested field of Toome flax, two hundred yards upstream of the patrol-boat mooring, when he heard the thin shattering percussion of the grenades. He had been waiting for the sound less than five minutes. His clothes were in the car, which he figured by now was picked up and driven to the rendezvous. He was lying with his chin on the back of his hands, his hands against the earth. The sound of the grenades came again.

He could see lights going on in some of the cottages near the road, and an occasional shape stepping out into the night, carrying a lamp. There was still no activity in the barracks of the Royal Ulster Constabulary, which sat back from the road halfway between himself and the Queensboat. His eyes squinted against the moonless night and he waited, getting the smell of the decaying flax as it came from the long trenches where it was weighted beneath the water with stones. The smell was pungent but somehow pleasing to his senses. He fancied he could almost taste it, it was that strong. The grenades sounded again and the barracks went alive with men who filled two vans noisily, waited for a brief while, then drove away in the direction of Antrim. By the time they drove away, all six of the grenades had been exploded and the diversion men should have been well free of the area.

When silence came again the American felt that the

smell and taste of flax was stronger than it had been and
he grew concerned in a detached and peculiar way, a way
that used to make him daydream while taking an examina-
tion in school or while playing football, that there was
something about flax which he should have understood and
that although he had a grand affection for it and what was
done with it, that at the same time his interest was lacking
some quality and had less to do with flax than it had to do
with himself and flax; and that Roddy whatever-his-name
was in the grave under the stone with Gaelic lettering was
mixed up in it as well, but also from the outside in, the
way it had been the night he was lightheaded in the Armagh
pub with stout and darts and singing. But these thoughts
came and went with great speed, because the silence after
the grenades and the barracks was the kind of silence he
recognized as having a sound of its own. He stood, held
the heavy box away from his body, and trotted with his back
bent low, the inflated inner tube hung over his shoulder
until he was on the bank of the river. He stopped there and
went down on one knee, looking everywhere in the field
of his vision.

The land all about him was flat farmland, even on the
far side of the river. Occasional whitewashed cottages
dimming their lights now that the noise was down. The
Toome bridge was not visible in the heavy gloom of the
night, but it was well fixed in his mind's eye. He had the
sensation, just before slipping into the water, of seeing himself in a motion picture.

The temperature of the river was cold almost beyond belief, and momentarily he felt he might not be able to get
on with it, the threat of foot cramps was so bad. But the
feeling passed and his flesh became numb.

The force of the current was strong and he carefully
maneuvered the twenty yards, into its churning center, keeping the inner tube ahead of him and being pulled along.
The solid weight of the box hanging down from his waist

was a surprise. He thought the water would have lightened it considerably, and now he grew concerned about his buoyancy once he had to let go of the tube.

The current seemed to increase in force and speed as he traveled further downstream. He rose and fell, bobbing with the tube, placing one hand beneath him every so often to check on the box, which thudded against his groin whenever there was a lunge to the current. He could hear nothing but the roar of the water, and it was almost impossible to lift his face clear of the spray to look around. He judged finally that he could not be that far from the bridge, and he began turning his body and forcing the inner tube to the left bank of the river, but it would not force so easily. He had miscalculated his speed and to move transversely in the current was almost impossible. He twisted the tube with a violent wrench and gave a hard kick, but there was still little change in direction and he swallowed a heavy amount of water. The bridge loomed ahead of him with great speed. He lifted his chin over the near side of the tube and saw the boat not thirty feet away. He took a deep breath and let go.

He sank at once, the weight of the box taking him under. But the force of the current was not as strong beneath the surface and he found he could maneuver. He came up with a struggle, glimpsed the boat ahead of him to the left about fifteen feet, then sank, pulling with all the strength of his arms in that direction. He was just about to surface again when he was struck with a dull pound directly on the forehead and knocked even deeper. His senses reeled and he reached out his hands coming in contact with a cylindrical shaft. He had hit the boat and was now beneath its keel. He pulled himself back against the current, his lungs empty and aching. His entire body was stretched out flat by the current in the wrong direction, but if he relaxed his grip on the shaft he knew he would miss the boat altogether. The pain in his lungs increased as he pulled himself along. When his fingers reached the propeller blade he sensed his brain ready to darken from lack of air. He grabbed the blade tightly with both hands and came up, breaking the tilting limits of the surface, swallowing air and water with great gulps. There was a pounding ring in his ears.

He rested his body, still under tension against the current, then shifted his hands cautiously to the heavy protective burlap hung over the stern. He could taste the thin half-sweet taste of blood and water running from his forehead. The bomb was still beneath him.

Once on the stern he made his way slowly to the wheelhouse, finding it exactly as it had been described and photographed, the deck hatch over the engine housing coming open easily. He held the wheel to steady against a sudden wave of nausea, then lowered himself into the engine spaces. He worked as quickly as he knew how, uncoupling the box from his belt, forcing it open painfully, then tripping the single throw switch from the timer to the caps. He placed the bomb just forward of the housing under the bilge pump. The nausea came again as he pulled himself up into the wheelhouse, and bent over to slide back the deck hatch. The hatch made a loud banging noise as it secured, and the American dropped flat and still.

There was no sound. He looked through the wheelhouse window at the bridge. As far as he could see in both directions there was no one. Not even a single constable. He went out on deck and forward to the bow, keeping below the gunwales to avoid being seen from the shore. When he checked the riverbanks they were deserted as well. As far as he could see there was no one probably even within binocular distance of the boat. He stood up, wiping the drying blood from his forehead, breathing heavily with the realization that there had been no risk. It might have been possible to drive a car on the bridge, park it, dispose of the bomb, and drive off again.

He looked without feeling at the grave of Roddy McCorley, and remembered leaving the cable cutters in his pants.

OK, he thought, that's that, and he went over the side off the bow without caution, and swam downstream out of the heavy part of the current until he came to the rendezvous.

When he crawled up on the shore, McAlear was there with the other two men. They were all of them smiling. McAlear came forward with a blanket, which he threw around the American's shoulders, and said, whispering:

"It seems to have gone very well. Is your head all right?"

The American nodded. He was handed his clothes, which he found himself too weak to put on without help, and was given a drink with a piece of chocolate.

"Good enough," said McAlear, "now let's get t' hell out of here."

The American felt the cable cutters against him in his pocket as he settled into the back seat of the car, and he turned to find the toothless one looking at him with a questioning expression. But he avoided the glance and closed his eyes with a feeling of sick rage.

IV

The name of the waitress at Kelly's Cellars was Noreen. She met him there at a quarter to nine, and she finished her day's work by bringing him a glass of John Jamesons with some port wine for herself. Her face was rouged and she wore red high-heeled shoes and rayon stockings. When she spoke to him he enjoyed the singsong of her Belfast accent, the way she stared at his American cigarettes, and the open manner with which she allowed her legs to touch his beneath the table.

"Y' know when y' was here t'other evening, I says t' myself, he's a smashin' lad for a Yank, and first off'e asks me out, I won't but say yes right off."

"And about dancing?"

"Oh, aye. Sure I hoped y'd ask that instead of the

pictures." She touched his calf with her heel. "Y' never get t' know a bloke in the pictures. How about one of them Yank fags there?"

He gave her the cigarette, lit it, drank his whiskey, and ordered another round from the new waitress. All along the whitewashed walls and stained beams of the bar were hung brass plates and pewter mugs. Their presence gave him a nostalgic pleasure.

"What's that y' did t' your head?" she asked.

"Bumped it."

"Sure on what, the end of a mare's hoof?"

"A boat. What's your pleasure in dance halls?"

"Oh, I don't mind. The Plaza's about the best. Biggest too. Don't y' think Sandemans is smashin' wine?"

They walked slowly and casually through the gray Belfast streets, past Donegal Square and the high-domed City Hall, the shop windows where Noreen pointed out certain inexpensive clothes and jewelry that had taken her fancy, for drinks again, over the sidewalk art chalked that afternoon by pensioners, beyond the newspaper stalls that were still full of the Crown's patrol boat which had been exploded in the morning in the middle of Lough Neagh, and the five mutilated bodies of the men who had been on board. The American slowed his step passing the stalls, read the headlines briefly, and moved on with a peculiar feeling of having had nothing to do with them. Noreen held his arm tightly, matched her steps to his, winked at him often, and smoked as many American cigarettes as she could. It was less than a week after the boat was blown and he was on leave. Her being with him seemed in the best tradition, and they stopped still another time to drink.

"Do you know much about flax?" he asked her.

"What the linen's from? Only that it smells t' holy hell when you go through the country."

"Would you like a drive after dancing?"

"Sure it's a grand idea. Find a stook of hay."

"Did you ever live in the country?"

"Do I look it?" She elbowed his ribs and laughed. "I'm a city girl like the man says, and content to stay."

She was foolish and the perfect woman for the time. He put his arm around her almost with relief and squeezed.

"Y've got a smashin' strength t' your arm."

"Do you like it?"

"Well enough. What do y' think of mine?" She made a muscle.

"It's grand," he said. "What about the rest of you?"

She giggled. "Now why would y' have any interest in that?"

They had been driving in the country almost an hour, with the music and noise of the dancehall still ringing in their ears, when the idea of the Armagh pub with the darts and singing occurred to him. They were feeling very loose from continued whiskey and wine, and the idea came to him obliquely, as if from a great distance in his memory. As they drove the girl kept her hand on his thigh, and every now and again she tickled him.

When he braked and turned off the lights outside the pub he could hear the men singing "Bridgit O'Hogan." The voices were heavy and thick in unison, and many feet were pounding the rhythm on the floor.

Her waist o'myself'd make threee,
an' whenever I'm standin' beside her—
me elbow just reaches her knee . . .

When the American opened the door with the girl the entire pub fell silent. Almost every man had a glass in his hand and the pub was crowded, smelling of fish and farming. The far end of the bar was gloomy in the haze of smoke and all of them stared incredulously at the presence of a woman in their midst. The red-haired man from the diversion had paused with a dart in his hand just before throwing it at the board. The American went to the bar

with the girl and said, "Jamesons and a glass of Sandemans port."

"Hey there, yank," said the red-haired man. He threw
the dart and came over to the bar. The silence gradually
left the rest of the pub, but the song did not begin again.

"We're in the wrong pub," the girl whispered with a
giggle.

"Nonsense," said the American. "It's exactly right." He
tossed off his drink and ordered another round, including
one for the red-haired man.

"Thank you kindly."

" 's OK."

He put his arm around the girl and maneuvered his way
through the men to the dart game. The toothless man was
also there, and sitting in a corner with his pipe was McAlear.

"Hello, McAlear," he said. The closeness of the room
made his head still lighter and he felt reckless. "I'd like
you to meet someone." He waved for McAlear to stand
and join them.

"McAlear," he said, "this is Noreen, ah . . ."

"Conlan," she added with a mock curtsy.

"Noreen Conlan, meet McAlear. Noreen is the spirit of
Ireland, Mr. McAlear, don't you think?"

The man neither smiled nor said anything. He nodded
at the woman.

"Don't you think she's the spirit of Ireland?" He drained
his glass and called for another. "Partition, Mr. McAlear.
The grand spirit and reason for putting an end to Partition."

McAlear took the pipe out of his mouth and said in a
low voice that was calm: "You were to stay in Belfast for
two weeks and not come to Armagh."

"I was just showing the sights to the spirit of Ireland.
She ought to get to knew the country, Mr. McAlear, don't
you think? How 'bout some whiskey? Does you good when
the nights be early like this."

The girl laughed, sliding her arm around his waist and

giving a flick to McAlear's cap. The American addressed
the toothless man.

"How about another song? That one about Roddy what's-
his-name, McCorley. A little Roddy McCorley."

The toothless man stared at him and put his darts down.

"C'mon," the American yelled looking around the pub,
"how 'bout somebody singing 'Roddy McCorley'?"

"Up Roddy McCorley," said the girl.

"Right. Up old Roddy McCorley. Who'll sing it for the
spirit of Ireland? All you people, somebody must know it."

There was silence again and everyone looked at them.

"A barrel of stout to the man who can sing it."

There was silence again.

The American picked up a vacant pint at the bar and
drank it down in a series of gulps. The girl pulled at his
sleeve, her high spirits fading in the silence and said,
"Maybe we'd ought t' find a pub with a little life."

"So nobody knows it?" he yelled. "Nobody knows old
'Roddy McCorley'?"

McAlear turned and sat back down. The toothless one
picked up the darts and began playing again, and some of
the others continued in their conversations. None of them
paid him any more attention.

The girl tugged at his jacket and said, "C'mon, yank."

He set down the empty pint and elbowed his way with
her through the crowd and out into the night, steadying
himself against her, then leaning on the fender of the car
and breathing heavily.

The first sensation he had in the night air was the smell
of flax on the wind.

THE FLAX
LONG RIPE

It made Dick absolutely furious that the "order of nature" could be so quickly and easily destroyed. Poets probably felt the same way when linen was first made from flax.

Dick felt it was impossible to write true romantic poems in the twentieth century, because the things that used to inspire them are being ruined. He felt he had to reach back in time in order to be pure about poetry.

M.F.

The flax, long ripe, was pulled that day.
Strong hands had torn it from the earth
To lie in rows beneath the sun.
The tea and scones had come at four
To let the men lie down among
The flax.

The wheat, not ripe, three fields away
Was growing strong and thistle free.
It gave a rattle, low and strange,
When breezes blew across the lough
And Sean came with a moan straight through
The wheat.

Mother's dead, he said that day.
And so they went away to lay
Her old bones down beside the church;
And when the banshees came to scream
The sons said go and pray, for our old
Mother's dead.

The flax, then warm, was put to rot
In water holes down by the heath
And then raised up to lie and dry
Beneath the sun until the smell
Of death had gone and they made linen from
The flax.

THE
MONTEREY
FAIR

This is all true—the whole thing. He mentions the Beverly Hills Hotel in here; we had come on just too weird for them at the Beverly Hills Hotel . . .

He loved being a troublemaker—and looking back, I'm glad. How boring not to be! But sometimes, then, I'd be embarrassed. I'd be mumbling and really furious, and he'd be whistling gaily all the while . . .

M.F.

One night last August, I was taken behind an old circus tent in Monterey, California, by a member of the John Birch Society and asked if I wanted to fight. I had returned to the United States only weeks before after an absence of two and a half years. I went to the fairgrounds with six other people in high spirits to see the fat lady, go on the rides, watch the preposterous sows, eat carnival food, have our fortunes told, and win a stuffed panda. In three days I was going to be married. The girl was Mimi Baez, I had brought her back from Paris, and since she was in Palo Alto, one hundred miles to the north, helping her parents to fill their house with wine and flowers, it seemed a good enough way to pass the evening. I was staying in Carmel at the house of Mimi's sister, Joan, the folk singer, along with a number of other people who had arrived, seemingly from all over the world. My own high spirits were intensified by this sense of international rendezvous, this coming together of old friends to celebrate a love affair we had chosen to make public.

Thomas Pynchon, the best man, had come from Mexico City, after dodging a team of *Life* photographers who would not tolerate his requests for privacy. The mysteries implicit in *V*, his novel, were causing the literary public to demand counterparts in his day-to-day life. Betsy Siggins, proprietress of The Club 47 on Harvard Square, had left her husband with the Charles River Valley Boys in Cambridge in order to travel west by train with Joan, who refuses to fly. Kim Chappell, Joan's closest friend and sometime secretary, was also with us, and a sunburned surfing friend of hers whom we knew only as Marty. Others were coming, some of whom I didn't know, and there was always the possibility of an extraordinary surprise, some splendid arrival out of earlier years.

The euphoria was delicious. In London and Paris I had always lived in flats and hotels the dimensions of which made it possible to touch at least two walls while standing in the middle of the room. I had spent the last six months in France writing scenarios for an obscure recording company that specialized in the transcription of fairy tales. To supplement that income, and the rare check arriving from an American publisher, I took character parts in the production of the scripts. I was the rabbit and the five of spades in *Alice in Wonderland*. I was a baby bear in *Davy Crockett*. I was Rip van Winkle. But the patient voyage back across the Atlantic, punctuated by apprehension over what we might find in our unsteady nation, and the journey overland in a borrowed Falcon, had put an appalling distance between those potluck Paris days and these of Stateside reality. From the first glimpse of New York haze with its excruciatingly familiar odor—a blend of incinerator fumes and damp cement mix—there was an uncanny sense that no time had elapsed since my departure years before. All at once, through an arbitrary act of will, I had again become subject to the rules, the manners, the convictions, the insidious fears that were marking the time of my country's uncertain life.

Joan, Kim, and Mimi helped alleviate those fears. They sowed the seeds of euphoria to come. It was not so much their state of mind, as beset by the symptoms of national moral decay as my own, but their ability to satirize the superpatriots, who were in all likelihood our common foemen. Each of them possessed an accomplished actress's ear for the commonplace, an ability to affect manner and inflection, which rendered the objective source ridiculous. Going out to dinner became less a method of satisfying hunger than an opportunity for the public assumption of middle-class roles. To ease our mortal anxiety over atrocities in Birmingham, strontium 90 in baby teeth, Barry Goldwater's photoelectric flagpole (Stars and Stripes triggered by the light of a rising Arizona sun), we could not put aside the vaguely hysterical need to change personality gears. Joan became Lois Faceless, wife and mother; Kim became Harriet Paralysis, cafeteria hostess; Mimi was Midge Motionless, Parcheesi queen of Kansas City; I was Fred Hodaddy, amateur golf champion; and so on. In Los Angeles, where we went to deliver the borrowed Falcon, we booked rooms on an impulse at the Beverly Hills Hotel and stepped into their cocktail-hour lobby wearing jeans and buckskin, carrying guitars, Joan barefoot. The entrance was packed with motion-picture people in evening dress. We spoke mock Arabic to the midget pageboy, drummed impatient fingers on the mahogany desk, and were actually surprised when told there was some mistake, no rooms were available, "The man who spoke to you on the phone was not authorized to make reservations," et cetera. While storming out and nearly knocking over a covey of canasta matrons, I turned to the girls and asked what went wrong. I ought to mention that we had been in the sun, that the Baez family is Mexican and dark, and I am part Cuban and dark. We had the attention of the passing women, and when their conversation fell off during the pause following my question, Joan answered in her Lois voice, "They're just not taking Negroes any more." The matrons' heads swiveled face front, their steps quickened, and their conversation picked up in intimate whispers. We walked the rest of the distance to our car in silence, trying to burn down the wooden doorman with the collective fire of our gaze, then drove away feeling conspicuous and embarrassed, because suddenly there was no one else to share the episode with. That night we went to a place called the Ash Grove and heard Mance Lipscomb sing the blues.

All of this happened before Mimi went north to Palo Alto to meet her parents arriving from Brazil. I returned to Carmel and settled into the business of waiting for the wedding. People were giving small parties with the right music for the time, riding me around in fast automobiles and new motorcycles, keeping my head high in the wind, fooling me into a reckless sense of freedom and an evasion of responsibility.

The headlines were always a little ahead of whatever destination we chose, however, and torpor was setting in. With an ad from the *Monterey Peninsula Herald* in my left hand and a glassful of Jack Daniel's sour mash in my right, I suggested we cheat the coming boredom, jump into the machines, and make it to the fair. Pynchon interruped his *Scientific American* reading, Betsy finished her drink, Kim and Marty came away from trying out some recently purchased bullwhips, Joan asked the young son of a widowed friend to join us, and we went off, dragging part of the way on Route 1, passing cigarettes and jokes back and forth at stoplights, singing rock-'n'-roll with the radio, and otherwise playing the game some people call California.

But as we parked the cars at the fairground (after being guided to spaces by unnecessary numbers of police), the lethargy threatened again. It was sympathetic torpor this time, picked up in sluggish waves from the groups that wandered about aimlessly in sports shirts and cotton dresses, limiting their sense of carnival adventure to the purchase of foot-long hot dogs and tutti-frutti cotton candy. There was no abandon, no lack of inhibitions, no noise, above all, no magic. I felt quite empty without Mimi, remembering nights in Paris when she had been able to transform the most prosaic scene into a bacchanal just by cocking her heel and dancing out into the street; or when we had gathered guitars at the Place de l'Odéon a little before midnight and sung our way across town, into the dawn at Les Halles, never once interrupting the music, trading verses with strangers, taking turns on the instruments, getting the truck drivers to abandon their endives and artichokes in order to twist through a chorus. But the absence of passion, the apathy in the milling Monterey crowds might even have discouraged Mimi, and this backhanded reflection actually filled a portion of the emptiness. We paid our dollar to an unsmiling Harriet Paralysis at the gate (which was guarded) and wandered in, unconsciously adopting the languid pace of those around us. Once inside, however, we noticed an occasional group with a little more spirit. They were teen-agers in packs, getting methodically drunk, laughing dangerously, surging toward this or that object of hopeful amusement. There was also a group of Negro boys loping along, smiling and afraid to smile, knowing if there were any genuine fun on the grounds they would find it, but not daring to look too hard.

We moved into the midway and bought tacos and beer. Pynchon coming to life with the tacos, not having had Mexican food in a couple of weeks, me being tolerantly happy that no one had ordered hot dogs or cotton candy. In the center of the food pavilion was the fair's only source of music, an electric-guitar band made up of three plainly dressed high school boys. We gave them a try. They played badly. The night was not looking well at all. Bart Creedon, the youngster Joanie had invited, came over and suggested in a whisper that we sneak off and win some pandas and dolls for all the girls. Kim and Marty had disappeared with containers of beer, Pynchon and Betsy had put on shades, and the panda suggestion seemed all right.

The fortune teller, whom we found on the way to the games, was drawing an interested crowd. Even the teen-agers were there on one edge of the circle, and the Negro boys on another. She was fat and blindfolded, her hands clasped behind her, standing on an elevated platform before a curtain inscribed with astrological signs. Her accomplice, a middle-aged man in white shirt and glasses, weaved carefully through the audience avoiding skeptics, provoking volunteers with his weak patter. There was nothing very mystical about them. They both seemed so devoid of any gypsy attitude, any sense of the exotic, they could have been drive-in bank tellers. The accomplice passed in front of Bart and me, grunted and moved on. I suppose we hardly looked the type. But on the chance of keeping some fun in the evening, I stopped him and handed over fifty cents.

Using the transistor pickup in his shirt, he asked my hometown, date of birth, and nickname. We had already noticed
a curious quality in the woman. As she was finishing up
with her previous subject, her voice had taken on an air of
the imperative and lost most of its sideshow condescension.
It was as if the remote vocabulary of psychoanalysis had
somehow placed her under a greater obligation to discuss
motives than to reveal simply the will of the gods.

After she had mispronounced my name and guessed at
my temperamental characteristics, I whispered to the accomplice that some of us were thinking of going to Washington, D.C., in a few days. Were the heavens favorable,
would the trip end well, and so on? To our quick surprise
his objective manner vanished. He moved his wire-rim
glasses to a more secure position on his nose and asked,
"You mean that parade, that mass nigger march?"

In spite of myself I coughed and scratched my face. "The
Freedom March, we call it."

He grunted and nodded at the woman. With the previous
subject there had been the predictable barker's inflection
in her voice, an attempt to ring in the stragglers and dis-
believers at the periphery of the crowd. This time, however,
her attention belonged entirely to me, and there was no
more than a subtle attempt at theatrics.

"You are thinking of a trip," she said, "a journey to an
important city. You intend to go there before very long."
She paused. "Yet you may not possess many of the facts
you ought to have before embarking on a journey of this
kind. You might be allowing your motives and your feelings to lead you into something uncertain. I believe you
have many friends and acquaintances who are also thinking
of making the journey.

"They are being led astray by emotions and they should
think again. There are forces at work, which you may not
be aware of, that make the whole purpose of the trip look
simpler than it is." Another pause. "Perhaps you ought to
reconsider your plans." She hesitated still again, this time

becoming aware that the personal tone of her advice was displeasing her audience. The teenagers had already moved off, and restless conversation was beginning. She summed up quickly: "The journey is ill-conceived." She nodded at the accomplice, who began talking to a new subject over the crowd's murmured reaction.

We hurried after the others to tell them what had happened. On the way to the fair, we had passed a billboard, which said: SAVE THE REPUBLIC. IMPEACH EARL WARREN. Just that same morning we had heard about the paramilitary civilians who were arming themselves with hunting rifles and bivouacking in the surrounding country on weekends to prepare for the coming invasion of the Negro-Jewish-Catholic-Marxist Alliance. The "fortune" told me was too strong for coincidence in this part of the world, and I wanted them to know what might be going on. Betsy, Pynchon, Kim, Marty, and Joan had joined up again and were just entering a long gauntlet of booths that faced each other at the end of the midway. Oddly enough the booths advertised, demonstrated, and sold a number of thoroughly noncarnival commodities. Teflon-coated frying pans, two-year hitches in the Marine Corps, polyethylene flowers. One booth was marked PEACE. It bore the familiar rebus of Sane Nuclear Policy, and contained placards and literature from all the committees on nonviolent action. I made a mental note to visit it later in the evening, a note made meaningless when I saw where our group was standing and why they had stopped.

It was another booth. It flew a banner, which said in very firm block letters, THE JOHN BIRCH SOCIETY. Beneath the banner, behind a counter of pamphlets and books, were three reasonably well-dressed adults in various states of activity. At the back of the booth was a large circular medallion depicting an American eagle. The potential energy of its oversized talons suggested it might have been the personal pet of the God of War.

Betsy was saying, "Oh, wow." Pynchon was hunching

his shoulders as if for protection from an overhead blow. Kim and Marty had their mouths open. Joan was expressionless. I was aware that something would happen before very long. It is not really possible to collect a number of creative people for an evening on the town and expect them to avoid forcing a tangible synthesis, or conclusion to events. If objective circumstance is not propitious, artistic people will invariably add what is missing, beginning with their imaginations and ending with physical action. Otherwise, they risk having the night end conventionally, with the subsequent chance of collective depression.

It is true we might have sidestepped any involvement with the people in the booth. We might have kept our respective cools, nodded at one another, gone on the rides, played games, ridden home in silence, and talked about it only over a nightcap. All of this occurred to me while we were standing there waiting to hear what Joan would say. Even the subject of the nightcap conversation ran through my head: How none of us had ever seen so overt a display of the society's intentions; how we had always assumed their membership was relatively secret, certainly never public; how there must have been extraordinary confidence in their ranks to move them out into the open so boldly; and how this confidence surely had its political feet on conservative California ground.

There was a challenge in the neon evening air; among us, Joan was the one who usually spoke out to set the pattern for what would follow. It was a matter of what she would say and how she would say it. I should also confess to the same breed of reckless exhilaration we had felt at the Beverly Hills Hotel. Toes might be stepped on, yes, but we seemed exempt from any but the most superficial reprisal —reprisal that in any case would only strengthen our opinion of the Birchers. Somewhat nervously I wished we were better dressed. Joan was in jeans and cowboy boots, Kim was barefoot, Marty wore an Indian sweater that covered him like a bearskin, Betsy also wore jeans and boots, Pynchon had borrowed my old red hunting jacket, and I wore a sweatshirt with the sleeves cut off. We looked pathetically easy to classify.

Joan stepped forward. People were beginning to gather behind us, recognizing a celebrity, and I wanted the first words to be as nonaggressive as possible.

"Do you have anything here on peace?" she asked.

The man did not look as if he believed the question. He said, "What?"

"On peace. Any of the books here?" She gestured at the neat rows of leaflets and magazines, which included everything from Robert Welch's *American Opinion* to William Buckley's *National Review*.

"I'm sorry, no." The man seemed puzzled. "All the peace stuff is down at that other booth. Just down the way there."

She paused and examined what was on the counter. A middle-aged, attractive woman sat by a table inside the booth, knitting, and another man arranged stacks of leaflets under the eagle medallion. People were gathering in curious dozens. The silence was uncomfortable. I moved to Joan's side. The man who had answered her first question was short, heavy, thin-lipped, balding, hook-nosed, and, surprisingly, neither blond nor blue-eyed. He was also not very much at ease. I had the feeling he would have preferred a quick consultation with his two compatriots, but everything had happened too quickly. Still, he was not entirely without grace, and he kept a smile, or rather the suggestion of a smile, impressed on this other, uneasy expression. We failed to learn his name, but later on we called him Ambrose.

"How come," Joan continued, "there's nothing at all here on peace?"

"That's not what we're here for," said Ambrose. The knitting lady nodded. The crowd behind us, in this short period of time, had swelled to extraordinary proportions.

"Why are you here then?"

Ambrose looked still more uneasy; and at that precise

moment, from the rear of the crowd, someone laughed. It was a teenage laugh, coming from too great a distance to have had anything to do with the conversation at the booth. But Ambrose was visibly provoked by it and he snapped back, "What are *you* here for?"

"I'm here because I believe in peace."

"I see."

"Do you?"

"We all believe in peace, right? That's what everybody wants." He looked around at the crowd. "Everybody wants peace."

"You really do? You *believe* in peace?"

"Yeah." He waited a moment, glancing back at the knitting lady and the leaflet arranger. "On our terms."

Pynchon made a grunting sound. Joan smiled—the kind of benevolent, self-assured, understanding smile that infuriates people with no desire to be understood. In a gentle voice that further infuriated the man she asked, "And what are your terms?" Behind us a loudspeaker voice was echoing over the grounds, speaking out the numbers in a raffle. *One thousand and twenty-five. Seventeen thirty-six.*

"What?"

Nineteen and seven. Zero-zero-one-four.

"Your terms," she said. "If you wouldn't mind telling, I'd like to know what they are."

"Right here," he said, holding up a handful of leaflets. "Anything we got to say is all right here."

"It's written down," said the knitting lady, picking up a stitch.

"You want to buy one? Nobody's stopping you."

"Yes," she said, still smiling, "I'd like to. How much?" The smile, in combination with the size of the crowd, the responsibility of having to say the right thing, to be clever and not lose face, nearly undid Ambrose. He was holding a pamphlet meant to be given away and he answered absurdly, "Two cents. Two pennies." He was more immediately distracted by the sudden appearance of a friend's face in the crowd. He put the pamphlet in the man's hand. "Here," he said. "Take it home and read it. Show it to the wife." But when the man tried to pay, Ambrose grinned and told him that it was free. It was a thoroughly desperate attempt to make an alliance with someone on our side of the booth, and it failed precisely in the spirit of its conception. Joan produced the two pennies and placed them on the counter.

Ambrose, of course, need not have worried about allies. There were dozens of them all around. But they remained silent, recognizing him as their spokesman. That was his function this particular night; that was why he was placed directly behind the counter instead of sorting pamphlets or knitting.

"We don't need your money," he said, "we know what your kind is up to."

"What?" asked Betsy, inching forward.

"We know all right," he repeated, grinning knowingly, signaling for assent. The knitting lady looked up and said, "We're here to sell those books and pamphlets, and I believe whatever you want to know you'll find inside of them."

"They don't want to know anything," said Ambrose.

"We want to know your terms for peace," said Joan.

"It's in the books," snapped the man, and his temper was less under control. During the pauses in the discussion— and they were longer and more loaded than I've indicated —I had been reading the titles of the books, and thinking of topics too recent to have been included. In the same vein, but with opposite polarity, the woman said, "If there's something you'd like to know and it's not in the books, go ahead and ask."

"Go ahead," said the man under the eagle.

"The test-ban treaty," I said, and they looked at each other. Another loaded silence.

"Yes," said the woman, finally, her knitting needle aside. "What would you like to know about it?"

"Only your position."

"We're against it," snapped Ambrose again. "That's right, isn't it?"

The woman repeated in a surprisingly humble voice, "Against it."

"May I ask why?"

"The communists have broken fifty treaties since the last war. They'll break this one, too."

"They will," said the woman. Their manner had changed slightly to include a feeling of shared, more covert information.

"You don't think it's worth the risk?"

"Risk is hardly the word for it," she said.

"Risk giving them a nuclear advantage?" said Ambrose. "Risk widening the missile gap?"

"Are you afraid of that?" asked Joan.

"You're damned right I am."

"Even if the treaty might change the way men think?" I asked.

"What does thinking have to do with it? They'll keep on experimenting no matter who sells us down the river signing a piece of paper. 'We will bury you,' is what Khrushchev said."

"He's already broken fifty treaties," repeated the woman.

"They'll test in secret," said Ambrose.

"Suppose we had faith?" I asked, taking a chance. "It's a reasonable Christian virtue."

"They're not Christians," said the woman, dissolving any ethical consideration with a pass of her knitting needle. "They're communists."

"What are you arguing for?" asked the man under the eagle. "You don't really want to learn anything from us."

"No, that's not true. I want to know what you believe in. If an expression of faith is less important than corrupting the teeth and bones of children, I honest-to-God would like to hear why."

"Where does that bone junk come from, anyway?" asked

Ambrose. "Dr. Teller says we can continue testing at the present rate and there'd be no danger at all."

"We can achieve a nuclear break-through," said the man under the eagle.

"I don't see anybody dying with bone cancer," continued Ambrose. "Where are they?" He gestured at the crowd. "I don't see any." His voice rose. "Show me where they are." He laughed and some of the crowd laughed with him.

"Oh, come *on*, man," said Joan.

"We just can't believe them, that's all," said the woman. "They have a history of breaking their word."

"They don't have any word," said Ambrose. "They want to bury us."

"Khrushchev came right out and said it," from the man under the eagle.

I tried it their way. "Most nations have been capable of deception at one time or another. Even our own. But by itself does that have to keep us from working toward something better?"

"That's what you say," said Ambrose, " and I can guess where you read it."

"Russia is an imperialistic, tyrannical power," said the woman, "trying to gain an empire."

"And America?" I asked.

"America?" from the eagle man, incredulously.

"Puerto Rico, Cuba, Panama Canal . . ."

"Cuba is ninety miles from American homes," said the man, reminded. "Ninety miles." People were murmuring. Pynchon and I turned to check behind us and were astonished by their number. The entire passage between the two rows of facing booths had been choked off, and free movement was nearly impossible. Police were moving in from both ends of the passage trying to find the source of congestion. Joan saw them, too, and pushed for some kind of final commitment before we were forced to move.

"So in order to keep them out," she said, "the Cubans

and communists, you're willing to start a war that's going to blow up the whole world?"

She asked it as a child might have. There was the same innocence of purpose and phrase. It was perhaps that innocence that blocked the man's ability to give a straight answer.

"If you're pushing peace," he said, "you go on down to that other booth."

"But what are you pushing then?"

"What are *you* pushing?" he mimicked.

"I'm pushing peace, right? What are *you* pushing?"

He was silent.

"Please, it's terribly important. Don't be afraid to say."

He was silent.

"Don't you know?"

A look of recognition came into his face, an expression of sudden, tactical knowledge. "Me," he said, "I'm pushing the John Birch Society."

"All right," said the first of the arriving police, "break it up. Nobody can get through here. What's going on, anyway?"

"If you want to know any more," said Ambrose surprisingly, "we can go behind the tents." A number of us looked at one another, then answered a quick "all right." He lifted a hinged section of the counter, coming through to where we were standing.

"Move along, move along," said another of the police. The crowd dispersed, some willingly, others with a grudge, as if something were unfinished, as indeed it was, while the rest of us made our way to that section of the fairgrounds that ran behind the tents; damp, weedy areas littered with old newspapers, paper bags, garbage cans, empty bottles. Being forced to go there, I was preoccupied by the conflicting sensations you so often have while being made to do something by an uneasy police force. First, injustice, because you know no malevolence was intended toward the society they are keeping you from; second, sym-

pathy, because you remember that milling, politically conscious crowds are the sleeping volcanoes mobs boil out of;
third, paradox, because it is not easy to understand the
logic of moving from the clarity of a well-lit midway to the
somber darkness of a vacant lot. The police seem to prefer
agitation in alleys. The subsequent violence is more traditional.

So we were again followed. But this time the crowd had
sorted itself out, and the stragglers seemed more interested
in the content of the argument than in any superficial proximity to the unusual. The carnival was running down at an
insulated distance. A number of cruising teenagers had
separated from their friends to join us, a few married
couples with buttons on their sweaters had given up Teflon-
coated frying pans to come along; there was a local Texan;
an anonymous Negro in his twenties wearing a suit; a boy
of seventeen who carried a tape recorder under his clothes;
and the core of the booth groups. The conversation had
changed during this shift of location, and a temporary
sense of truce prevailed, allowing both sides a chance for
forced intimacy. Inevitably, most people gathered around
Joan, pulling their earlobes, coughing, hiking their trousers.
But Ambrose did not join in. He kept his brooding distance,
walking alone, apart from everyone, including his two col-
leagues from the booth. I forgot him and began to join a
conversation. Presently I noticed him gesturing at me with
a finger. He seemed to want things less public.

It was a reasonable notion. The talk around Joan was
still evasive. On the chance that he might cut across semi-
official jargon and deal with our difference in terms of his
more personally closeted terrors, I took the invitation.

We strolled out of earshot of the others, under a grove
of sycamores, which marked one boundary of the grounds.
"All right," he said finally, "how do you want to settle
this?" I assumed he was talking about the separate points
of view on the test-ban treaty.

"Through mutual understanding," I said.

"There's another way to work this out," he said. He'd
stopped looking at the ground and was watching me instead.
Not at my eyes but the way I was standing, my hands in
my back pockets, weight on one foot.

"I don't understand," I said.

"You come over here insulting hell out of me, cooking
up trouble, and think that's all there is to it? You want to
settle it some other way?" He grabbed my shirt front and
made a fist.

"What?" I asked.

"Just tell me," he said. "Just let me know. Nobody can
see us here, c'mon." He let go of my shirt front with a
gesture of disgust and breathed heavily, deeply. He had
decided not to hit me that way and was looking for some
species of provocation besides his own, something more
tangible than a verbal position. But from me, he was not
about to get one. I relaxed my body and expression openly
and asked him cautiously, "You wanted me back here
to fight?"

"Come on, beatnik."

But I was not coming on.

"We know who you're working for, what your plans are."

It was his show. I said nothing more.

"They send you in here 'cause they think we're not ready,
that right? You don't think we know you're coming or
something?" He laughed and looked around him to make
sure we were still alone. "Well, we know, all right. We get
our own briefings on your party line. You want to settle
this some other way, I'm ready. You say the word."

I did not say the word. He seemed aware that I was
finished with him. If in spite of this he meant to hit me, I
was resigned to taking it. There was no chance whatever
that he could purge his fear by knocking me over, but I
am certain he felt a lesson might be learned. He could
always learn it from his pillow later on, however, so I gave
more thought to the relaxing business and watched the different parts of his face, in particular the corners of his

mouth and how they trembled. It is one time that I felt no alarm when threatened by another man.

He spat on the ground and walked away. I thought he was going to pick up one of the headless ax handles adjacent to the grove of sycamores and come back. It was a stupid, selfish fantasy, one that included a mind's-eye picture of my bandaged skull being nursed at the local hospital (although it was partially redeemed by the knowledge that I still would not have fought back). But he did not return. He spat again, glanced at me once, and kept going, joined suddenly by two friends I had never noticed. They had been waiting behind the trees.

Later on, I wondered whether his departure had been spurred by my resignation, some quality implicit in offering both cheeks. I also wondered if he had considered our positions irreconcilable. But at the time of his leaving, I believe he simply considered me beneath his contempt. I believe he was revolted by my proximity to his person. I believe he might have thought about explaining the unwashed blood on his fingers.

I stayed there under the tired trees, watching the littered ground and feeling weary in the marrow of my bones.

When I rejoined the rest of our party they were growing tired as well. The seventeen-year-old boy was no longer making any attempt to conceal his tape recorder. The local Texan was bragging about the number of black laborers he had allowed into his Southern home over the years. The young married couples played with their conspicuous buttons. (IMPEACH EARL WARREN. REPEAL THE INCOME TAX. THE PRICE OF LIBERTY IS ETERNAL VIGILANCE.) Joan was asking them not to be afraid. And the young Negro who wore a suit was telling of the suspicion and hatred and dread that filled a white drinking place whenever he entered, and women were present.

"You're just making that up," said one of the wives, a blonde.

"Woman," he said, "you ask your husband."

I prefer to think that she did. I prefer to think that in the quilted intimacy of their night she turned to him and inquired about the reasonableness of their fear. I prefer to think that the teenagers examined their arbitrary decision not to collide with the Negro boys when they saw each other going home across the empty grounds. I prefer to think that the button owners were aware that they recommended the legal procedures of repealing and impeaching rather than the burning of a Reichstag. With the fairgrounds now somewhat trampled, the booths dark for the year, I prefer to think that the creatures of darkness—if they are half the devil's—are half our own; that whatever goes bump in the night can be made to find a door; and that eternal vigilance is rather an expensive moral price to pay for liberty. Liberty is something we still might be giving away.

LET'S CHOOSE UP SIDES AND PLAY THE GAME OF LIFE

One of Dick's earlier poems. All of his younger work seems less cynical.

"Thistled kiss . . ." He really loved Dylan Thomas.

M.F.

Do all things come to this?
A young girl, after lunch
(we don't know why she is,
or how),
who wonders down a path
between some trees.
We'll put a lake
beside her. Autumn now,
she thinks, the leaves
are umber, russet, goldenbrown.
How perfectly divine,
how splendid (she might
say to someone strolling by her side),
there is no war, no thistled kiss.
All things might come to this.

Perhaps an empty street somewhere.
A narrow, cobbled alley
where a lion prowls alone.
No other sound or motion
save a bird's quick wings
above his mane. Black, flapping
things they are. They sail
upon a somber wind that moans,
that howls, that bears
the broken banners from the Maginot
and Troy. A fetid, dusty wind
along a street where people
fear to roam. Beware.
Perhaps things go to there.

Or shall we choose a landscape
less confined? A blend

of ash and loam where hordes
of demons (on occasion)
sport with elves.
Where articles upsetting
to the mind and eye,
go drifting nonetheless
upon the flawless surfaces
of glacial lakes.

THE GOOD
FORTUNE
OF STONE

Dick did go off once into the mountains and ended up chasing a wolf, and, again, I don't know where the reality stopped and the fantasy began. I first read the wolf story in a letter he sent me; he would send me stories or poems that way in the form of letters. Later he would rewrite them. He wrote this one a lot of times; there's even a version of it in Been Down So Long It Looks Like Up to Me.

This is a very deathy story: it seemed to be in so many of the things that Dick wrote about— that he was preparing to leave. He was so mystical that I still don't know what to think: how much he knew about what . . .

M.F.

Caro m'è il sonno e più l'esser di sasso
Mentre che'l danno a la vergogna dura,
Non veder, non sentir, m'è gran ventura;
Però non me destar, deh! parla basso.
MICHELANGELO, FROM THE SCULPTURE "NIGHT"

I

Leukemia.

Creeping with unsensed shudders and easy rhythms, it brought the man back into the woods to hunt for the first time since last he had seen the fetid eggs of death. When he lay or sat waiting for it, or if the sense in other things caused him astoundingly to forget, it darkened his loins with the crowded heat of fear; it sprung upon him moments of reeling exhaustion as it continued sowing the small meticulous seeds of doom along the seam of his aging blood.

The late-night chill in the core of his heart. And the cold of winter, simple and familiar to the senses, loud with the nature of its elements or silent in the old primeval way, but never mute. Not the same as what was engendered in his bowels, nor any degree of it. A separate species, a different kind of thing. When he took his walks alone he was in control of the winter precisely as far as he chose to involve himself: if the wind changed force or direction or the temperature dropped low enough for snow to fall, there were signs in the snapping bark of hardwoods or the weight of spruce boughs under wetter, heavier loads, or the movements of animals. He could fail to perceive the signs, but the fault would be his own, or the failure to have come into the knowledge would be his. There was no treacherous procedure in the winter, no worm in the fiber of being, or wild gray multiplication that pulsed apart from will and reason.

Chaos and pestilence had a single name and the name was leukemia.

He'd come to the woods, this man, to his family's clapboard cabin, which had been built by a lake for summer pleasures; and a woman had come with him, one who liked him well enough, who slept with him and made him grand meals with exotic spices, and breakfasts of fried fish that were caught through the ice, food that he ate with no heart for it, but out of old habits and customs, and inert respect for life still humming in another person. They never spoke of love except at the time when they went to have one another; or on the heavy leather couch in front of the fire, and only then because it seemed precisely the proper and traditional thing to mention, a careless, self-indulgent group of comforting words. Her name was Kristina, and she knew nothing of the disease. He wondered, in the early days of accepting its presence within him, in the detached and somber manner that was an active symptom of the disaster, why he failed to say anything, imagining it was some lack in her, remembering moments when he had been extremely close, waiting for the utterance of a sudden phrase on her part, some half-expected shift in inflection or idle gesture of a hand which might seed the crystal of the truth. But he came to realize there was nothing so profound in his silence. His regard for the life she still possessed so safely—the ovarian potential hovering in her sounder blood —made him afraid she would repel the concept of a man with death spilling loose in his system, the fleshy length of his body against hers, the risk of some dark conception each time he went within her.

He walked across the frozen lake now, back from a long morning stroll without his weapon, his duck boots going down over the ankles in snow, but not touching the ice, which must have been three, maybe four inches thick. Here and there he passed small circular areas where the woman had made holes for fishing and left markers of hardwood limbs. The lake was a large one, going on in length for nearly a mile, its crusted shoreline beginning everywhere at the abrupt end of the somber pine woods, its whole plainlike whiteness hovering, as if suspended in the saddle of the land. In its center was an island of a taller breed of pine, the tops of the trees rising over the chalky mist that blew always from the frozen surface. Ermine and weasels ran out to the island in the dawn, and vanished.

In this late morning the woods were pleasant for walking, cold enough so that two hours was a sensible limit, but with enough December warmth still left from the sun's declination to keep breathing comfortable. In another week, perhaps two, he thought, the warmth would be gone for the rest of the winter and his breath would be short and weak in the woods, making it even harder. Just before crossing the lake, the exhaustion had reeled through his blood, causing him to lie and rest, and in the humming silence he fancied he could hear the snow soften and melt under his weight; he remembered that if a man sat in some species of acoustical room, where the quiet was absolute, that he would hear the scream of his own nervous system.

Going back over the surface, the symptom vanished, he relaxed, then forgot and gave his memory over to the new things he had learned during the walk. The partridges, for one, were living in the trees and no longer foraged on the ground—he had crossed through a small spruce grove and seen them there before they whirred away, making him snap up his arm to follow silently as if there were sights on his shoulder and fingertip. The foxes, for another, seemed to be getting careless (or perhaps they were not careless and had instead some complex plan), but they were coming down very close to the lake after mice. He had stalked their nervous trails as they tripped into elliptical paths, sometimes clawing at the roots of a tree where the earth was exposed and the snow stained with clay. The herded deer beds were new to him as well, and the beavers' work, although he learned less about the beavers, since theirs was an activity accomplished months before when the dam was not frozen for him or anybody to walk on and decipher.

With the snow beginning to squeak under his boots and the wind rising suddenly and then subsiding, he also thought about the very peculiar tracks he had seen near the deer beds. They were tracks such as a dog might make, but a dog would have visited the lake as well, or come to inquire about the cabin. And there was no other person within twenty miles, easily, or if there were, it was not the right weather for a dog to travel that distance. There was another possibility, of course, because the winter was driving the deer together and they all made their beds on the moss in one place, and their spoor was very strong, but he didn't allow that possibility any strength in his mind.

He knew the name, but he knew it remotely, so if someone else, the woman Kristina, say, should ask him what tracks they were, he would probably answer a dog's. Still, he knew what animal it was.

As he neared the camp the wind was swinging down out of the taller mountains that were shadows on the horizon, spinning the snow off the lake and up into the air like the runners on an alpine sleigh. It was an empty thin wind, foreboding, and remembering its counterpart in another time, he was glad of the coming warmth.

There were snowshoe tracks leading away from the cabin as he neared it, and inside a note held over the top of a glass of whiskey by a rubber band. There was no fire in the fireplace, but the wood stove had been left roaring and the heat was strong in the one large room. It reached his face, swelling his cheeks slightly as he removed his parka and read that she had gone some miles up the trail in search of a wet doe and two fawns they had seen foraging the week before.

He was disappointed at her absence, wanting her there not only for the company, but to be able to tell about the partridge, that if he'd been carrying the weapon, he could have taken one or two, since they were in the trees now, off the ground in a way he'd just learned. He drank the whiskey,—it was Irish whiskey,—a kind he preferred for its harshness in his system, and when the small tumbler was empty he poured and drank another one, knowing that because she wasn't there, the partridge thing would go untold forever, small a piece of information and knowledge as it was.

He warmed the Irish in the glass between his hands as if it were brandy, and drank it slowly.

Outside, the bark on the hardwoods was snapping sharply as the temperature changed, and he felt glad and secure being near the old cast-iron stove, the wood burning down and glowing in its belly. Soon it would be far too cold to snow, and people in that part of the country would spend whole days like this, a quietly enduring aspect of an indoor silence, reading, doing small chores, the very miniscule facets of which would define the satisfaction of their afternoons.

He lay down on the couch and wound the phonograph machine by his head, putting on the top record, but pausing a moment before dropping the needle as a hint of the exhaustion overtook him again, and passed as suddenly. There was with it, for the very first time, the amorphous clutch of despair while he sensed the depth and silence of the woods for many miles around, the Irish warm in his chest, and the sensation of something or other finally being finished up.

> *Put an-other nick-el in,*
> *In the nick-el-o-de-on,*
> *All I want is lov-ing you . . .*

But the voice on the record was gone now and the room was gone as well. There was no cabin or woods or hunting, but only a cemetery in his mind where two young men had gone with a gallon of wine, freshmen in college, and they stood just under the swollen barrel of a memorial cannon, watching the place in the sky where the sun had gone down and where there still shone a green and blue and ochre glow. The bottle was near to empty and they stood unsteadily, their arms about each other, to keep from toppling. He saw them clearly in the same section of his mind that had had the sensation of something being finished, one of them with the same face he had now, only the lines were not there at the corners of his eyes when he smiled, nor was there that other face under the one seen first, the other which said this man has lost a thing called youth. In that remotely functioning part of his mind he watched these two boys stand apart and hand the almost empty bottle back and forth, tilting it at a sharp angle against their lips and snapping it away so as to protect against spilling any, coughing a little, perhaps laughing. One of them he knew was himself, and the other was David.

A nearer part of him, a part which would also have spoken the name of the animal right away if it had been given that name to hold, said *David is dead*. But the part that saw the cemetery still heard him talking, his speech thick and drunk and punctuated with heavy pauses. The man whose face was swollen from the heat in the old stove, in whose chest the liquor warmed, who had just snapped the bottle of wine away from his mouth to keep it from spilling, he watched the glowing pulse in the sky away west. The military gravestones were at least twice his own age, and being there with them was not the same as being in another place of graves. These were faceless and lost, strangers, shades, they had no menace or portent in their idle grass and failed flowers. There was no meaning to his feet pressuring their earth, and no care for the bottle his friend took and tilted against his pursed lips.

A toas', David had said. To all the los' times.

An' vanished regimes, the other boy had added.

To los' times and vanish' regimes, then.

Sure thing.

Walking down the small slope from the cannon's perch,

stumbling as they went, David doing a teetering about face, the other boy holding the bottle tenderly in his arms. David was saluting.

What think of all these ol' fighting men? he asked.

Pretty good, 'Tenant.

'Tenant?

Cap'in, then.

Much better. Yep. What think of these fighting men?

Damn good men, Cap'in.

Bet your butt. Cream of the fucking-A crop, you know?

Begging Cap'in's pardon, we better not stay 'roun' here too long. German all over place.

Quick thinking, 'Tenant. Thoroughly correct and necessary. Sufficient. Have a little drink, then retreat.

Advance, corrected the other man. French Army never retreat, if you follow me.

The captain did another about face and took the empty bottle from his lieutenant.

Wha's that for, Cap'in?

Grenade.

Oh.

Couple Bosch over that rise.

Sure thing.

Lying there on the leather couch, his face still tingling from the glowing metal of the old stove, he remembered David taking the bottle by the neck and heaving it in a high arc over the cannon, and the strange thing that happened, the silent flash lighting on the horizon, then another and still another, jerking suddenly on the couch and gazing in surprise at the young officer next to him, with no thought to distant fires or heat lightning, and the fear of being attacked still again.

They're coming, yelled the captain, and both men dove to the ground. Slowly, in the mind of the young man now, there began the distant thudding of artillery, and the gentle flat pumping of machine-gun fire from over a fair distance. He heard once more the sudden groan.

I think I might be hit.

Hold on, I'll get you.

Drunk and unable to stand steadily, the Irish still warm, and hearing the hardwoods snapping with a pang in the cold, the lieutenant lifted his friend clumsily around his back and carried and dragged him up the slope past the cannon to something safer. He eased him to the ground carefully, looking in different directions for a corpsman.

S'no good, said the captain.

I don' understan'.

S'futile. I'm dead, ace, you been carryin' dead David last hundred yards, if you follow me. Futile an' ironic.

No.

Abs'lutely futile.

> *I'd do anything for you,*
> *Anything you'd want me to*
> *All I want is hugging you*
> *And music, music, music . . .*

He turned and watched the empty glass at his side. It was catching the stunned reflection of the snow outside and gleaming wildly, the only source of light in the room. If the girl Kristina had been there, he felt he might have called her over to him and moved his hands up under the angora of her sweater to touch her breasts. The lust remained in him for some moments, and he courted it before removing the glass to a shadow, and taking down the Marlin automatic from the gun rack on the redwood wall. Just at that moment of touching the glass, of controlling its reflection and altering the observed condition, and hearing the voice squeak on from the old phonograph, it occurred to him to clean the weapon and have it ready for the afternoon after his nap, even though he had not hunted or desired to kill anything since the last time he had seen and tasted the oxide of death.

Later on, when he was close to sleep in the bed with his face turned down against the pillow, his mouth damp and the eiderdown insulating the generated warmth of his changing metabolism, he remembered the name of the animal again; it was unadorned and salient in his brain, as certain as the faceless worm in his blood.

II

In the afternoon the sun was gone, the fire had cooled in the wood stove, and a chill hovered in the air as the man drew his first waking breath. When he went outside with the ax he wondered if he might have been wrong about the signs and the quantity of warmth left in the early part of the winter, since as soon as he left the protection of the camp and its trees, he had to lean against the wind, which came against him icily, and tuck his chin against his chest. It was coming straight out of the north, piercing his sweater and woolen shirt. With no sun, a numbing gray-whiteness swarmed in the field of his vision. The pine island stood like the specter of a fortress, the heavy branches sagging away from fifty-foot trunks. The thin lines of tracks that the weasels and ermine had made at dawn were now anonymous furrows, light creases lying on the snow. He swung the ax through the air and it skidded into the ice, discoloring the surface of the freeze and sending small splinters sliding away. He swung again and again, until he was through to the water; then he widened the hole so that it was large enough to receive the enamel water bucket. He'd been chopping through the same hole now every day for thirteen days, and each night it had frozen back a good quarter of the way. But this time it had frozen through to the surface again, and when he lowered the bucket, his lungs were aching slightly from having to breathe the thinness of the freezing air. He rested for a moment when the bucket was full, and stood looking out the mile to the far shore, then up beyond the island to the land in the north. It was like a plain, roaring, devoid of the living, and he

remembered the reservoir at Chosin just as he heard the
sound of the animal.

It came only once and he looked carefully in its direction,
but saw nothing. He waited a moment, his ear to the moan-
ing wind, then picked up the bucket and walked back to
the cabin, the snow squeaking under each step.

The hot tea was good and did the job of bringing him
around. He poured more of the water into a small Dutch
oven and placed it on the wood stove, then added a few
chipped logs and stoked the fire. The jerked venison, a gift
from a hunting neighbor some twenty miles away, was in
the cupboard, and he took down half a dozen small pieces,
placing them on top of the oven to steam, then chewed
them slowly, not caring particularly for the heavy smoked
taste, but liking, at this precise time, the idea of their being
venison. He put an unmeasured amount of Irish in the
second cup of tea and took down the box of shells to load
in his cartridge belt for later on. He started to fill the belt
completely, but then thought for a moment, considered his
purpose, and only used five shells, three of them slugs and
two buckshot. He drank the tea slowly and listened to the
bending of the trees, their bare tops soughing in the wind.
And in his mind he saw another man, this one with wrinkles
folded in the corners of his eyes, but still without that other
face beneath, the one that said youth was no longer there.
The man was waiting at Koto, thinking of the passionless
cold that had wrapped its skinny arms about the sun and
sent the throbbing night to visit those who had ignored the
wisdom of Genghis Khan, and come to make war in the
winter, on the land of the Mongol. The wind from the
north whistled into his ears and he was watching the last
of the ice-covered bodies being rolled like logs into the
great open grave, the wound in his side giving a surge of
pain with each heartbeat and rush of pumped blood. The
world of other days surrendering all existence in the minds
of those who had come down from Chosin. He watched the

frozen foxholes as men slumped together like sacks of coal, sleeping bags over knees and feet, hoods pulled up on their helmets, and the frozen, useless cans of food lying spilled in the snow around them. They neither talked nor moved nor did anything but turn more deeply and irrevocably into themselves as the cold settled down on the land with primeval silence. He heard again the shepherd's horn and saw the face of each man as he wondered why his mind had chosen to make such a sound. Whistles shrieking wildly in the night, bugles pulsing flatly into the rendered air, the sounds of chaos falling together in a stunned cacophony of howls and moans. They all had heard.

He looked down at his hand by the cup of tea, the hand that months before would have been sooner to move, and he watched it lift the receiver of the sound-power and heard the faltering, young, and familiar voice ask for flares, for light, for something to let them see.

The tiny pops in the air as the fields and childsize paddies beyond the reservoir were lit by the sputtering globes that swayed gently beneath their parachutes. The shadows taking form and substance. As far as vision and sense prevailed, the waves of Chinese soldiers marching abreast, one wave behind the other, chanting songs as they came, little quilted toys padding along on a corrugated floor. In the trenches, the men waiting, moving their fingers, shifting weight, prodding the vestigial streams of memory. He watched the flares burn out, then the red image on his eyelids where they had burned.

The stove was hissing as some of the water boiled over and bubbled down on the hot metal.

He removed the cooker, looked for a moment at the impression his form had left on the soft old bed, then lifted out the few remaining pieces of venison, wrapping them in foil and dropping them into the outside pocket of the parka, which hung on a nail. The hands of his platoon were extended before him, each one cut and bleeding, torn open from trying with futility to dig in the frozen crusts of earth.

Four miles from the beginning of the retreat the point man
was veering to the left of the snow-covered trail and leading the column off in the wrong direction, the line of shuffling men following mutely, senselessly, without thought.

The pine island was a shade, an echo of substance; he
watched it through the window and saw himself running
along the column, yelling at each face as he went, with
none of them turning to hear the wild words that were
sucked out into the wind and dissipated. He was at the
beginning of the line now, stumbling in front of the point
man, his lungs aching viciously from gulping the freezing
air, holding the man by his shoulders, screaming into his
stunned face. The other hooded figures, shuffling forward
with their heads down, their eyes fixed on some vanishing
aspect of the trail at their feet, do not know the line is being
stopped and each man is bumping into the man ahead
of him.

One by one they are all falling down in the snow.

As they lie there, breathing quickly, long-range sniper
fire falls among them. They are rolling or crawling to cover,
and he sees another man who is himself, the tears frozen
to the lashes of his eyes, kicking and pulling at them to
get the line moving again. The wound in his right side has
reopened and is bleeding silently, soaking his uniform.
Time is a function of some other existence and they use
the bodies of the dead for sandbags. The bodies are frozen
and make thick crunching sounds as they are struck by
small-arms fire. He looks from the pine island to the place
where he had heard the sounding animal, and across the
barren, swirling surface of the reservoir there comes a fragment of the Army that had tried to stop the Chinese in the
East. The first ones to reach him have no hats and their
ears are blue and purple where the frost has gnawed. Hands
are shredded and torn. One man, pitching to and fro as if
drunk, talking sweetly to himself and grinning, is walking
barefoot in the direction of the enemy.

David is lying down, his blond hair matted with ice,

his body pumping blood out on the snow. He is bleeding to death from a deep wound, because now the plasma is frozen.

Grenade.

Oh.

Couple Bosch over that rise.

Sure thing.

> *Closer; my dear come closer.*
> *The nicest part of any mel-o-dy*
> *is when you're dancing close to me . . .*

He took the parka down from the nail, put it on, and felt for the pieces of venison in the pocket before getting his gloves. The unthawed chunks of food and unboiled snow have brought disease to the intestines. There is no solution then, or treatment for the diarrhea, only the absurdity of soiling oneself while marching forward. Near Koto a large number of Chinese are surrendering blindly to the troops that retreat from them. Some are wearing sneakers and their feet are frozen solidly through to the bone. The ones without gloves or mittens are stuck to their weapons, and he remembers their faces, wrinkled, the narrow eyes, the startled, unbelieving expressions when in order to disarm them, their fingers are broken away from their guns.

The bodies at Koto, so many rigid, loglike trunks, are gathered together and dropped and rolled into the one large, open, frozen hole. He is at Hamhung remembering without passion or desire the ship that squats in the gray morning of the bay, its whistle blasting and blasting and blasting over the harbor, the ship that will take them all away to some other place. He is in a cabin in the mountains, a cabin thrown up out of trees and stone and minerals, the products of some quiet, enduring patience, and cosmic good fortune, remembering the small boy with his mother, meeting the troopship at San Francisco, the son of some soldier coming back, making a little gun out of his thumb and forefinger and saying, "Bang," pointing at each of the men edging down the gangplank with their bags balanced on their shoulders, "Bang, bang," clicking his thumb.

He looked at the matches and compass by the coffee tin, did not pick them up, then lifted down the Marlin automatic which felt familiar, despite the years, in his gloves.

There was little change in the wind or temperature as he stepped out onto the lake and began walking across, the snow screeching under his boots. It must have been fifteen or twenty below, he figured. He stopped once, the blood chilling slightly in his veins as a splintering crack, the thinness of a needle, shuddered up the lake with a gurgling roar. It happened twice again before he reached the opposite side and he estimated how quickly the temperature was falling to make the ice contract with such ferocity.

On the other shore the wind was milder because of the trees, and he moved inland rapidly, only glancing at the familiar knolls and rises he once had used for resting. The nap had given him strength and the exhaustion did not course through his system. Whenever he came upon a section of spruce he changed his pace, taking steps as silently as possible and staying downwind of the trees. In the third heavy grove he looked into the snow-weighted branches carefully, and came to a stop. The partridges could just be seen then, two of them sitting up in the boughs, and yes, they were eating the buds. They remained that way, their crops bulging and swollen under their small beaks, until a pine cone shattered suddenly beneath the weight of his foot and they whirred up, dipping slightly toward the earth before breaking away at right angles to their flight. He followed them with the gun, leading at what he thought to be the proper distance and making a noise in his mouth just at the time he would have fired if the gun were loaded and he wanted to.

There was silence again, except for the gusts of wind through his hood, and he put the three slugs in the chamber first, then the two buckshot, taking an unexpected pleasure in the sound of the clacking bolt. He was close to the deer beds now.

New fox trails could be seen along the way, and he decided finally that they were becoming careless after all, and not merely bold in their hunger; the beaver dam was the same except for some rabbit leavings here and about, and he paused to breathe deeply, not from any swirling in the blood, but just to have the pause, to close his eyes for a moment and wonder should he give any more thought to what he was doing. He sighed (still, it was more than a sigh, it was an exhalation that surrendered a subtle aspect of his purpose) and moved over the last rise before the deer bed.

A young buck was standing there quite still, waiting to see what had been coming, its head stretched high and forward, its ears cocked. The sight of it that close was astounding. Behind the buck was a doe; they turned together when they'd seen him, moving delicately at first, then bounding off, and he could feel the thudding of their hooves on the earth up through his boots as he followed them with the gun, not firing, but only to see how he might have done it.

Then there was another sound behind him.

It came from beyond his side and as soon as he heard it he realized why the buck had waited. He turned slowly, bringing the barrel of the weapon around in front of him, while an ironical section of his mind asked, *Now what is a German shepherd doing in the woods?*

The animal looked at him, its gums curved and trembling above its fangs, snarling and backing away with almost imperceptible motions. At one point it gathered position in its hind legs and lowered its head as if it would spring, but at that moment each facet of the man's body and mind knew it for the wolf, and his thumb was sliding the safety off; his forefinger was squeezing the trigger as the weapon moved from below his hip, up along his body, toward his shoulder. When it was above the hip one slug was away, tearing the bark from a tree just by the animal's head as it bounded off ferociously. The second skidded into a moss-covered stone by the deer bed, arching up into the horizon. The third was fired from the shoulder, and just before squeezing the trigger the man's mind was trying to get inside that of the animal thinking *One more, he only has one more; I'll veer to the left then break away for the heavy part of the swamp*; and he squeezed, saying death as the slug tore into the animal's rear and ripped through its intestines and stomach, coming to rest just under the throat. The animal tumbled over with tucked paws, its nose plowing the snow up ahead of it; then rose with a falter and lumbered off sickly into the swamp.

The man stood and gazed after it, his body chilled and perspiring under the heavy clothes, the smell of powder and oil acrid in his nostrils. He looked for a moment at the three red cartridges ejected into the snow next to him, then he walked to the place where the animal had been hit. There were some small pieces of gray and white fur scattered with the blood that was steaming slightly and melting down into the snow.

He slid the safety back and looked with a faint but controlled smile in the direction of the cabin. He patted his pockets, then realized more fully that he'd left the compass and matches behind. He remembered them next to the coffee tin.

Somewhere a barefoot man was walking on the ice in the direction of the enemy, talking sweetly to himself and grinning.

He waited, as if expecting an utterable phrase or quick gesture, then felt his fingers for circulation before turning and trotting off into the swamp in the direction of the wounded animal.

He ran that way for a great distance, trying with difficulty not to interrupt his pace, and looking ahead cautiously to plot his path so trees and heavy brush might not stop him. Here and there were signs where the animal had fallen or rested from weakness, but always, when it had risen again, the tracks began at a far enough distance to indicate that it had bounded away rather than limped.

After crossing the third swamp he could no longer run and he leaned heavily against a tree, his lungs aching harshly from the exertion and thin air, the beads of perspiration frozen into the alpaca lining of his hood.

When he had rested enough he began again, walking this time, and chewing one of the pieces of venison for strength. The tracks were steadier now, with less blood; there was no mistaking the animal's desire for the deeper and more silent parts of the woods. From the strain in his calves and thighs he knew much of the distance had been uphill, but all sense of direction was gone and there was no brightness in any one part of the overcast sky for him to tell where the sun might have been.

At the end of two hours of walking he felt the cold very deeply in his fingers and toes; it became necessary to flex them continually in order to keep the circulation alive. He finished the remainder of the venison while still moving, and looked often at the darkening sky. He'd thought at first it was just the thickness of the swamps and the trees blocking out his vision, but he was in an open place where if there was any good daylight at all, he would have seen it. He wondered then how long he had been gone from the cabin. Behind him there was very little way of knowing which were his tracks and which were impressions made by the patches of snow that fell in lumps from the heavily laden branches.

He thought, *Will my body betray me?*

It made a kind of amorphous sense that if he kept after the animal, the animal being sick and looking for a place, some breed of synthesis would be evolved, some distillation achieved. He tried to think again in the animal's head, but it no longer worked. He could only approximate: The wolf had been doing what all of his species did; something that had nothing to do with wolves, some interloping surprise, had interfered and arranged its fate. If the wolf failed to comprehend this interfering thing, but realized the defeat, then it would go away and find a place.

He continued moving slowly until the sharp sound of snapping hardwoods, the prolonged shriek of the snow beneath his boots, and the swollen depth of the cold in his extremities told him that it must be close to thirty below. He had not found the animal, but it was impossible to go on.

He stopped in a section of the swamp where the spruce trees abounded, and he broke away a number of the younger, softer boughs. It was hard to see now, and he chose his spot quickly, feeling foolish for having to hurry, laying the boughs next to and over one another. One of his ears was causing him great pain and he pressed his teeth together as he worked on, hoping it would numb quickly.

When the boughs were all arranged he took his parka off completely—all around him were the sounds of the frozen evening with their whisper of the rising night, each of them alone, barely perceptible in the shuddering howl of the wind.

Should an animal throw back its head and utter a cry, the sound of its voice would be sucked up into the sky, dissipated, and lost. The man lay back on the spruce boughs to rest from the rushing fatigue, pulling the parka up over his body and shoulders like a blanket from childhood.

He kept the gun near his side in case the wounded animal should come to find him out. The buckshot was still in the chamber.

Then for a long while he thought of nothing at all.

The wind heaved through the treetops as if at some greater distance. Once he changed his position and that was when the sound of the animal came closer, from the edge of the swamp. He wondered about the place that a hurt and wounded thing sought safety, if it had a name.

One by one they are all falling down in the snow.

If he fell asleep too quickly the animal might come and eat his face. In time he became warmer and more comfortable, and he thought he saw a pearl, small and gleaming, arch up into the night and drop down into the silent abyss of eternity. He was ready to turn over on his side when he saw it, but another sound came to him, one which he had been hearing for some minutes but had not accepted. It was louder and stronger now, a yelled question, the sound of his own name. He rose on an elbow and saw the flashlight poking a shaft of light through the trees. He watched it with sinking heart and recognized the voice of the woman, Kristina.

Even after he realized she had found him, he did not answer.

"Are you all right?" she asked, coming up to him. "I heard the shooting."

Her voice, the sound of its life, stunned him. He stared at her without speaking, the image of the pearl fading in his mind's eye.

She stepped closer and asked, "Is anything the matter?"

He thought of her body, of her womb, and feeling nothing move within him, he lifted the weapon and let the plane of the barrel swing across the woman's middle. But he did nothing more.

"Why are you lying there?" she continued. "You're not hurt, are you?"

CELEBRATION
FOR A
GRAY DAY

This poem I love. This is where the title of our first album came from. It was a poem before it was a song; and it was never a song with words, just an instrumental.

It's an old poem; I know because it was printed the first time I saw it, in 1963. I was so impressed; I'm really glad it's in the book.

M.F.

Be quiet now and still. Be unafraid:
That hiss and garden tinkle is the rain,
That face you saw breathe on the windowpane
Was just a startled cat with eyes of jade—
Cats worry in the rain, you know, and are afraid.
The nervous laugh that creeps into our room
Is throated in a voice beyond the door.
We hear it once and then no more,
A distant echo tumbling from its loom.
Our time is measured in another room.

We know days pass away because we're told.
We lie alone and sense the reeling earth.
(You whisper in my ear it has some worth)
And I lean near to keep you from the cold.
There are so many things that must be told.
I speak of lost regimes and distant times,
And mooneyed children swirling in the womb,
And legless beggars prophesying doom,
And afternoons of rain spun into rhyme.
(The patter of the rainfall marks our time.)

As does the waning moon. Or muted sun.
As do the nodding gods who ride the sea.
For even now, alone and still with me,
You sense the bonds that cannot be undone:
Our pulse is in the rain and moon and sun,
We take our breaths together and are one.

BAEZ
AND DYLAN:
A GENERATION
SINGING
OUT

This came out in Mademoiselle *when we were all in Newport. Dylan read it when we were all sitting out by the pool, and he said in private to Joanie: "Dick is one of the only people who knows what I'm all about," or something to that effect. Which Joanie in private told me and I in private told Dick.*

That was really nice and it may well have been true. Dick was a little jealous: Dylan was much younger and getting a lot of attention; he was spinning miles around Dick in success. It got to Dick —that this younger person was able to do it in a bigger way.

M.F.

When Bob Dylan drove across the Berkeley campus with his songs in a hip pocket and a station wagon full of friends, it was as if the undergraduates had been whispering of his imminent arrival for months. They seemed, occasionally, to believe he might not actually come, that some malevolent force or organization would get in the way. From north into Oregon and as far south as Fort Ord, near Monterey, college-age listeners had found time to make the trip, secure tickets, and locate seats in the mammoth Berkeley Community Theatre. They had come with a sense of collective expectancy, some attracted by already implausible legends, some critical of an idiom that seemed too maverick to be substantial, but most with an eye to taking part in a passing event that promised more than usual significance for their generation.

Each of Dylan's concerts this past year had had a way of arousing the same feeling. There was no sensation of his having performed somewhere the previous night or of a schedule that would take him away once the inevitable post-concert party was over. There was, instead, the familiar comparison with James Dean, at times explicit, at times unspoken, an impulsive awareness of his physical perishability. Catch him now, was the idea. Next week he might be mangled on a motorcycle.

The Berkeley performance did little to set anyone at ease. It often looked as if it were calculated to do the opposite, as a result both of its haphazard form and the provocative nature of its content. There were songs about the shooting of Medgar Evers, the Mississippi drowning of Emmet Till, the corporate tactics of munitions executives, even a fiercely cynical review of American war history called "With God on Our Side." Dylan appeared as usual in well-worn clothes, said whatever occurred to him at the time, and sang his

songs in no particular order. When he surprised everyone
by introducing Joan Baez from the wings, the students were
electrified. Their applause was potent, overwhelming, unmit-
igated. Had a literary audience been confronted by Dylan
Thomas and Edna St. Vincent Millay, the mood of aesthetic
anxiety might have been the same.

To professional observers—and I talked to a good many
—this mood threatened to overreach the abilities of the
unassisted performers. They spoke of the fragility of the
two people on stage, the lack of props and dramatic lighting, the absence of accompanying musicians, the banality
of costume. A writer from one of the new folk magazines
told me, "They can't be *that* confident, man; sooner or later
they're going to play a wrong chord." But he was talking in
terms of show-business proficiency, while the performers
themselves were concerned with more durable values. They
never doubted their capacity to equal the ovation and, if
anything, they felt applause was a dubious reward for
their efforts.

They claimed to be there not as virtuosos in the field of
concertized folk music, but as purveyors of an enjoined
social consciousness and responsibility. They believed they
were offering contemporaries the new musical expression
of a tenuous American legacy, a legacy that threatened to
become the most destructive and morally inconsistent in the
nation's history. They felt the intolerability of bigoted op-
position to civil rights, the absurdity of life under a polluted
atmosphere, and they were confident that a majority of their
listeners felt the same way. "I don't know how they do it,"
said a San Francisco columnist, "but they certainly do it."
When they left the stage to a whirlwind of enthusiastic
cheers, it seemed that the previously unspoken word of
protest, like the torch of President Kennedy's inaugural address, had most certainly been passed.

Significantly, when Joan and Dylan are together and
away from the crush of admirers and hangers-on, the protest is seldom discussed. They are far more likely to putter

with the harmonies of a rock-'n'-roll tune, or run through
the vital scenes of a recent movie, than consider the tactics
of civil disobedience or the abhorrence of biological war-
fare. Like many another person in his early twenties, they
derive a sense of political indignation from the totality of
every-day conversations and media that surround them—a
process more akin to osmosis than ratiocination. And because of this subjective approach to the problems at hand,
metaphor is better suited than directness to their respective
dispositions.

"I don't like the word 'bomb' in a song," Joan said one
evening, watching a fire in her sister's small Carmel cabin.
The flames were the kind that hissed and crackled, causing
small coals to pop, and sometimes explode with surprising
violence. They seemed to reinforce her feeling that simple,
explicit reference to heat and radiation was too easy to
slough off, that this never evoked anything more than
superficial interest and sympathy in an insufferable situation. Speaking or singing with regard to megatons, fallout,
strontium 90, nuclear deterrents, overkill ratios, genetic
mutation, all in so many facile phrases, might have been
necessary for raising the initial indignation of the populace,
but it was certainly not sufficient. "People don't listen to
words like those," she said. "They hear them, sure, but they
don't listen."

Certainly popular American reaction to these concepts
had already proved, on the whole, nothing short of apa-
thetic. A more meaningful vocabulary was needed to loosen
fundamental feelings. Students across the country were
helplessly aware of this fact whenever their civil or political
protests were met by blatantly bureaucratic response from
public officials, elders, and even fellow students. Posters
scrawled with "Ban the Bomb" or "No More Jim Crow"
were invariably treated with a disdain that belied any awareness of the gravity of the causal situation. The students,
seeking a more profound language and finding such language in folk music, looked to folk musicians as their

spokesmen; and the musicians said and sang what they could. Last year, however, the vivid and topical imagery of a self-styled Midwestern folk-poet finally lent their arguments more vigorous meaning. And even from the point of view of the bureaucrats, this meaning was difficult to evade.

"It ain't nothin' just to walk around and sing," Dylan said; "you have to step out a little, right?" We were strolling in the pre-dawn London fog a year and a half ago, six months before he made the now historic appearance at the Newport Jazz Festival. "Take Joanie, man, she's still singin' about Mary Hamilton. I mean, where's that at? She's walked around on picket lines, she's got all kinds of feeling, so why ain't she steppin' out?"

Joan quite possibly had asked herself the same question. As much as any of the young people who looked to her for guidance, she was, at the time, bewildered and confused by the lack of official response to the protesting college voices. She had very little material to help her. At one point she was enough concerned about the content of her repertoire to consider abandoning public appearances until she had something more substantial to offer. Traditional ballads, ethnic music from one culture or another were not satisfactory for someone whose conception of folk singing extended so far beyond an adequate rendering. Her most emphatic song was "What Have They Done to the Rain," and she was, one felt, more personally moved by the image of a small boy standing alone in a tainted shower, than by the implication of the remaining lyrical content.

By May, 1963, however, she had a firsthand opportunity to hear Dylan perform at the Monterey Folk Festival in California. His strong-willed, untempered, but nonetheless poetic approach to the problem filled the gap and left her awed and impressed. Moreover, by the time she had finished going over the songs he left behind, it seemed his lyrics would finally provide the substance for her continuing role as a soulful representative of the generation, a young woman whose very function seemed defined by an ability to mirror alternatives to the malaise of the times.

Meaningfully enough, the highest personification of these social concerns was not indifferent to Joan's role. Just weeks before the Dallas assassination ended an era of Washington style that was based in part on an implicit acceptance of contemporary arts, Joan received a telegram from Lyndon B. Johnson asking her to perform for the President. Since that time, the invitation was renewed, and on May 26 she sang for President Johnson at a Democratic fund-raising show. Yet, it speaks for her place in the company of essentially interpretive artists that she has never strayed very far from the sensibilities of those closest to her age.

By living the life many university students would like to live, were it not for the daily concerns of textbooks and money from home, and by spending most of her public time in and around the nation's campuses, she has had no trouble keeping a half-conscious finger on an eager college pulse. Young people are very much aware that she drives an XKE and that it has been in the repair pits an inordinate number of times. So much so that a recent *Channing* television show used the car as an insipid symbol of the paradox of high speed and homely folk tradition. Some who live nearby are also used to seeing her chug down the Big Sur coast at midnight with four dogs in a red Jeep, to watch the moon above the Pacific. To most students it comes as no surprise that she is refusing to pay 60 per cent of her income tax, a figure that corresponds to the government's allotment for defense.

Occasionally one gets the feeling that people try too hard to relegate her to a premature immortality, and the subsequent rumors are in kind: She has come down with a mysterious paralysis and will never sing again; she has been arrested at the Mexican border with a Jaguar full of narcotics; she is living with Marlon Brando on a Choctaw

Indian reservation. In what many would call the alarming
calm of her California surroundings, the exoticism of these
stories seems absurd.

It was to her home in Carmel that Dylan came last spring
just after the Berkeley concert. He was on his way to Los
Angeles in the station wagon, traveling with Paul Clayton,
once the most recorded professional in the folk revival;
Bobby Neuwirth, one of the half-dozen surviving hipster
nomads, who shuttle back and forth between Berkeley and
Harvard Square; and a lazy-lidded, black-booted friend
called Victor, who seemed to be his road manager. They
arrived, bearing gifts of French-fried almonds, glazed wal-
nuts, bleached cashews, dried figs, oranges, and prunes.
Here again the legions of image-makers might well have
been disappointed by the progress of the evening. How could
so volatile a company get itself together without some sort
of apocalyptic scene dominating the action? Instead, Joan's
mother, visiting from Paris, cooked a beef stew. We talked
about old friends, listened to the Everly Brothers, and finally
got Clayton to do a number of songs that few others can
sing with such understated composure. The only overt reference to Dylan's music came when Joan said she might want
to record an entire album of his songs, and he told her
"sure thing."

The college student's reaction to Dylan has been somewhat more complex than their acceptance of Joan, however.
It was clear from his initial entry on the folk scene that he
was neither as musically gifted and delicate, nor as con-
sistent in performance as she. Yet Robert Shelton, now the
editor of *Hootenanny* magazine, predicted that these very
qualities would contribute to his popularity. "He's a moving target," Shelton said in New York, "and he'll fascinate
the people who try to shoot him down." In the beginning,
when he was better known for his Huck Finn corduroy cap
than his abilities as a composer, he jumped back and forth
between Boston and New York, developing a style and

manner that brought the manifestation of the pregnant pause
to uncanny perfection. Some still found a discomforting
similarity to Jack Elliot, or too much affectation in his
droll delivery; but everyone agreed his smirk implied a
certain something left unsaid, and that whatever it was, if
he got around to letting you in on the secret, it would
be worthwhile.

It developed that this something was his writing. In no
time, Dylan nearly abandoned established material for songs
of his own composition. The transition from one to the
other was nearly imperceptible, since he had the good sense
to keep his overall cadence within the framework of fa-
milar traditional music. He begged and borrowed from the
established ballad styles of the past (in some cases quite
freely), from the prolific works of Woody Guthrie, from
the contemporary production of friends like Clayton. But
the stories he told in his songs had nothing to do with un-
requited Appalachian love affairs, or idealized whorehouses
in New Orleans. They told about the cane murder of Negro
servant Hattie Carroll, the death of boxer Davy Moore, the
unbroken chains of injustice waiting for the hammers of a
crusading era. They went right to the heart of his decade's
most recurring preoccupation: that in a time of totally ir-
reversible technological progress, moral amelioration has
pathetically faltered; that no matter how much international attention is focused on macrocosmic affairs, the plight
of the individual must be considered, or we are forever lost.

Such a theme has often been associated with the output
of folk poets; in fact, since the time John Henry laid down
his hammer and died from the competition of the industrial
revolution, they have celebrated little else. But even including the dynamic figures of Guthrie and Leadbelly in this century, no creator of the idiom has ever received such a wide
cross section of public attention. It is quite possible that
already, within the astonishing space of a single year, Dylan
has outdistanced the notoriety of still another spiritual fore-
bear, Robert Burns. And like Burns he has the romantic's

eye for trading bouts of hard writing with hard living. He often runs the two together, courting all the available kinds and degrees of disaster, sleeping little, partying late, and taking full-time advantage of the musician's scene in New York's Greenwich Village, where he keeps a small apartment. Using a blowtorch on the middle of the candle is less aesthetic than burning it at both ends, but more people see the flame. He can dip in and out of traditional forms at will, shift temperament from cynical humor to objective tragedy, and never lose sight of what people his age want to hear.

This wanting is in no way a passive or camouflaged matter. It is part and parcel of a generation's active desire to confront the very sources of hypocrisy, which in early years deceived them into thinking that God was perforce on their side, that good guys were always United States Marines, that if they didn't watch the skies day and night, the Russians, Vietnamese, North Koreans, tribal Africans, and Lord knows who else would swoop down in the darkness and force them all into salt mines. Dylan feels a very critical trust was betrayed in these exaggerations. He feels further, in what amounts to a militant attitude, that it is up to him to speak out for the millions around him who lack the fortitude to talk themselves.

Because he speaks for them, undergraduates in many ways seek to identify with his public image, just as they have with Joan's. They search for the same breed of rough Wellingtons and scuff them up with charcoal before wearing. They spend weekends hitchhiking, not so much to get somewhere, as to log long hours on the road. I've even come across an otherwise excellent guitarist and harmonica player from Fort Ord who tried a crash diet with Army food in order to achieve the necessary gaunt look. The image, of course, has shifted with Dylan's increasing maturity. Some fans are reluctant to accept his early attempts at playing with his past. Last winter, an article in *Newsweek* went to great pains recalling his middle-class upbringing in Hibbings, Minnesota, and alluding to a prior, less attractive

surname, which had been removed by the courts. After the
Berkeley concert a nineteen-year-old girl in a shawl told
me, "He has a knack for saying what younger people want
to hear. It's only too bad he had to change his name and
not be able to accept himself." I reminded her that she
liked his music, but she went on: "People want an image.
They carry it around to make their scene look more important. There're so many guys wanting to be something
they're not that Bobby is a nice alternative. At least he
has individuality."

The seeming paradox between name-changing and in-
tegrity is significant, and his admirers enjoy possessing a
certain amount of private information and using it against
him as insidiously as they try to hasten Joan's premature
immortality. But he has done something they will never
do: stepped so cleanly away from his antecedents and into
the exhilarating world of creative action as to make the
precise nature of an early history look insignificant. Behind
the college students of America today, no matter what
their protest against segregation, injustice, and thermonu-
clear war, are the realities of their parents, the monthly
check, and their hometown. *The Freewheelin' Bob Dylan*,
as the title of his second album sets him up, lives in a world
that is the realm of their alter-ego.

But in the meantime the word still has to be passed, and
both Joan and Dylan go to the campuses to make sure that
it gets there. After the evening of the French-fried almonds
and beef stew, both of them journeyed into Southern California—Dylan with his friends in the station wagon, Joan
in the XKE. There was some anticipatory talk of getting
together at one or more of the concerts, but circumstance
was not propitious, and they went their separate ways. Dylan stayed at the Thunderbird Motel in Hollywood, drifting
out to parties and local folk nightclubs between engage-
ments; Joan stayed with friends of the family in Redlands,
lying in the sun, going to bed early. She sang at her old
high school one afternoon and was moved to tears by the

standing ovation. When she did an encore, her mention of
Dylan's name brought cheers. That same night, he returned
the compliment to a devoted audience in Riverside.

It could be said that during these respective performances, as with each of their concerts before predomi-
nantly young crowds, their specific relationship to their
generation is most unhindered and best understood. They
utter a statement of unmistakably mortal grievance against
what they stand to inherit as a result of the blunders of
their immediate forebears. In the one case this statement
is from the source, in the other through interpretation, but
in neither is there any distance between expression and experience. To the young men and women who listen, the
message is as meaningful as if it were uttered in the intimacy of their own secluded thought.

WAITING
FOR NEWS

Dick wrote this in Paris. He was very deathy when he came back there from England; it had been so cold, and gray, and he was full of morbid remarks.

It's just when I met him.

M.F.

There is within us all, my love,
the small gray bag of death.
A plastic sack, twisted
at the ends and sealed.
It chooses, on its own,
the hour of release.
Yet we can set small cells
to gnaw, to tear and puncture
of our own accord;
secretly to spill
the fetid contents at
a trickle, or a drop.

Last week there was a morning
when the sound of hooves
and sudden cries drove me
from an ocher sleep
and tricked my hand to searching
for your side.
What news had failed to tongue
my ear sought solace in the currents
of our room. I stirred and listened
to the hum of nerves and fibers
echo from the running walls.
There, against your pillow,
lay some damp. An oval mark
just where you mouth might be.

This trickling death, I know,
is mute and neuter
to the rhythm of its host.
Each drop is anaesthetic,
bald, inert to sense.

Still, the ease and pleasure
of the pin prick we instill.
A function being served
while afternoons of ceiling-
thought are wiled away:
that darkness fills the waiting
loins of time.

RETURNED FROM ENGLAND

*(Along the Quai
des Orfevres)*

On the Quai des Orfevres.

The Seine running like a gray and tepid vein in the mind of the city.

But running nonetheless. In London you are far less conscious of the Thames.

At Westminster Bridge, yes, because of the Houses of Parliament, of Big Ben. At the Tate Gallery because after leaving the sense-wearying confines of a museum you must look somewhere to ease and refresh the mind's other eye, and the exit fronts on the river. But the cautious, collective brain of the city fails to mind its presence. The same really in New York, with the East River and even the Hudson. Manhattan is the dominant entity; its northness & southness, its crosstownness, but never its bodies of water. New York schoolchildren are always astonished to learn they are dwelling off the mainland of the United States. Something insecure in the discovered geography. As if at any moment the land supporting the floors under their desks might tilt over sideways and slide into the sea.

Chicago denies the lake to its pedestrians. The automobile has priority, but at best (accepting the function of the automobile), that priority is transient. Eventually meaningless.

The Seine, like the Liffey, is never an afterthought in a consideration of the city. You are on one bank or the other, no matter how far from the quais. You are relative to the Pont Neuf or the Pont de Alma.

Last week Mimi and I stood on the Quai d'Orsay and watched (with many other Sunday watchers) while the young firemen in aluminum helmets sank

hooks into a floating object and lifted it free, drip-
ping, onto the bank under a tree. It looked to
everyone like a log. But it had achieved some un-
nerving quality of saturation, some water-thick
degree of viscous flexibility. And together, with
the other watchers, we at once recognized a
bloated leg attached to the lower half of a body.
The body had been severed at the waist. A hun-
dred yards downstream, a group of patient wine-
faced elderly men sat with pipes and caps and
warm shoes, and fished with long, weathered
bamboo poles.

In a while it began to rain.
I thought a good deal about death.

(from RICHARD FARIÑA'S diary)

We come from winter's nightmare sheets,
loud with lies to soothe the gray
and staining fiber of our lungs.
Out of terminals numb with time
and tea and damp wool clothes,
thick with huddled men and gloom;
loosed from fat and black-toothed women,
flesh in useless folds
(staring with the oxide taste
of doom and dreamy sorrow
on their tongues, at nothing),
purged tradition-wise by pain
and raw with expiation,
we come to break our ties.

"I mind the boulevards,"
the young girl Kristin whispered
(close against my ear for fear
of stirring seed among the loins
of huddled men and women),
"where the trees are swollen
wild with sap. You eased
away the stillness with pink wine."
And crumbled pastry
with an idle thumb. We watched
the all-night faces, white as mushrooms,
wrinkling in the sun.
"You've noticed how the Seine can change,
the current force, and then the hue.
So odd to see the *clocharde* woman
tumble from the walk and sink.
'Drinking gasoline,' they said.
And sinking like a stone."

The gentle swelling of her coat,
the billows in the folds,
and then the plunge, as if
the woman dove for bottom,
hurried to the silt and wrack
of still another room, teasing
us above a tilting limit
where the circles bulged and ebbed
away. "There is no simple way
to love," you said.

And now, from many littered
rooms, the mock design
of reason traced on walls,
the unborn children flushed
like refuse underground,
we come to stand alone.
"Just there the *clochardes* sleep,"
I heard you tell
(tell to keep the sense
in other things apart),
"close against the open grates
that face beneath the ground.
The rising heat is good
and keeps them warm."
We strolled the Tuileries
with lazy steps. And paused
together, looking. There the
statues writhed and posed
some definition, stood their patterned
ground and cast no shadows
in the muted sun.

I mind an afternoon,
but not an afternoon, a dawn
that eased its light upon
my crowded cells, that grew
in silent force and unsensed motion

through the opiated blood
and tricked some aging memory.
An afternoon, I thought, last year,
and saw an empty street
where dry and brittle papers
tumbled in the wind; a lion
stumbling on the cobbles, paws
unused to corrugated plains,
a night bird reeling in the air
above his head, squealing
with its open beak at cells
too narcotized to know
the sound of doom.

"We must make love," you said
(and led so I might come behind)
the day we saw the blond young man
screaming there before the public building,
loud, enraged, the only words,
"Algeria, Algeria!"
Then tear the spongy muscles
of his side with sharpened blades,
hit and stab, and plunge again,
spilling out the secret of mortality,
the gray and fibrous innards of
his time. His bird-voice wailing
all the while, his trembling hand
arching like a pendulum
to stab, and stab again.
You touched me once
when he had done.
You turned aside.
"We must make love,"
you said, and I thrust seed upon
an angered sphere
before we paused
to go our separate ways.

AMERICAN
AFTERNOON

You can see why Dick wanted to live in Europe, away from America. When you're a stranger away from home, you're someone special, or as he put it, exempt.

M.F.

The woman in the orange sunsuit was supposed to be some kind of special personality. That was what they all said at the lunch counter where Bunny Sue Johnson worked. Bunny Sue Johnson heard them say it this way: "She's one of them panelists or something, you know, a nem-sea." Bunny Sue never watched the quiz panel-type shows, but she heard them sometimes when the set was too loud and the sound came from downstairs in the living room. She was especially interested in the nem-sea part since that was in a way like being an actress. Now she was thinking of the woman in the orange sunsuit because it was Sunday.

One thing Bunny Sue Johnson would have known anyplace, even without the papers or a calendar, was Sundays. Mostly from the special quiet in the air and all the people who hung around like they were expecting something to happen. It was even more like that in early summer when city people were only just beginning to arrive in their town. There were other ways to tell, of course, like the smell of frying ham and Canadian bacon and the stiff peculiar manner the family had of behaving during breakfast. Cigar smoke, too. But even without thinking about the particular things, there was still this feeling in the air that made you want to go out and do something like visiting, or maybe take a long ride in the Dodge.

The family always hung around in the living room with the papers instead, which didn't have any appeal for her. And her clock radio that Dominic bought her never had anything on but religious programs and organ music. Which wasn't so bad if you heard it actually in person like at Radio City, but with preaching or the afternoon romance shows her mom listened to, it was very depressing.

Thinking about the woman in the orange sunsuit was

what got Radio City into her head. She planned it that
someday she would be Discovered and brought out West to
make movies. Everybody in town knew this was her special
idea so she had to make sure it came about. Once, the year
before, when she was still in high school, she went into
New York City with a bunch of other girls on a weekend-
excursion bus and deliberately got lost from them. She had
strolled around on Fifth Avenue looking at what buildings
might be best for her suite after she was Discovered. She
had almost said hello to one of the doormen, like she
passed by regular and was a familiar figure in the area,
but she didn't have the nerve. You could probably do that
if you were a nem-sea. Probably this woman lived in one
of those buildings herself. And maybe since she had come
to the town early in the season, Bunny Sue could catch her
attention and be Discovered.

Now that things had gotten quiet after breakfast and the
family was in the living room with the papers, she felt restless. She wanted to go someplace. There was that fountain
she had seen in Rockafellow Center with the Golden Statue.
That was the place. The more she thought about the patio
court with the big sun umbrellas and things like afternoon
cocktails with the glasses tinkling, the more exasperated she
became. If only New York wasn't so faraway a place.
Finally she thought she'd go crazy and she got out her sunglasses to go for a walk.

When she reached the front door her baby brother,
Andrew, came running up to her, wheezing, tugging at her
skirts and asking if he could come along.

"I'm only taking a short walk, honey, and coming right
back."

"That's OK. Harry's . . . in the back . . . yard doing . . .
manoovers."

His breathing was all choked up. That meant her other
brother Harry had been marching him around in close-order
drill. Ever since Harry had seen *Beyond Glory* with Alan
Ladd he wouldn't hear of anything else until he could get

to West Point. Here he was, already just out of high school, a year and four months younger than herself, and still carrying Doc Blanchard's picture folded up in his wallet. By now it was probably so scrunched up that it would break if he tried to open it out. He was too stupid to go anywhere, let alone West Point. Anyhow, it was Andrew got the worst of it. Only eight and what good did it do his asthma to be marching all over the backyard? As long as Harry paid him off with hot fudge sundaes at the Eden Reef Fountain, the dopey kid would have marched around the Gray Wall of China. So she said it was all right for him to come.

When they got away from the houses and closer to the main part of town, Andrew held her hand. It used to bother her when he was more bratty and not so sick but she didn't mind any more. Sometimes she even felt sad inside of her, like she was a mother and her kid had polio and was depending on her. She imagined this as Andrew held her hand. The streets had more people than usual for a late Sunday morning, too, and having those people watching them walk together (the poor mother having to suffer with her crippled kid in his brace beside her) made her a little proud, so that after a while she felt better that he'd come along.

As they approached the far side of town, closer to the ocean, there didn't seem like very much to do. Most of the people walking around were only out to get the paper, or else just coming back from late church. There was a crowd of kids outside the Pappas' drugstore, but she wouldn't be caught dead going over to them.

This was the big trouble with Sundays. You got so that you'd go crazy sitting still in the house, and then when you went outside there was nothing to do anyway. One of those little cars like some of the city people had would make the difference. She'd get out there about eight in the morning and tear all over the place with her shoes off and her hair blowing to beat the band. Maybe she'd tear through the middle of town, honking when she went by Pappas' and screeching the tires on the corner near where Dominic used to live. That was the kind of fast feeling everyone wanted to have. So that you weren't cooped up in one place and you were able to have the wind blowing around you in some big open plain. When she was Discovered she would only take roles of ladies wanting these same things. Queen of the West, or Southern Belle looking out over the wide fields of cotton and magnolia.

When they reached the old coast guard tower there were only a few people on the beach and nobody swimming. Andrew skipped a little ahead of her, but came back as soon as the sand got in his shoes, and she helped him empty them out. She asked if he wanted a soda. He said a hot fudge sundae at the Eden Reef, and that is where they went.

Inside, Bunny Sue picked a booth that faced the door. She could look at who came in that way and maybe get an idea of the latest fashions like they showed in *Vogue*. Thinking about magazines reminded her of *Screenplay,* and after ordering the sundae and a black-and-white soda, she purchased a copy along with a *Plasticman* for Andrew.

"Do you see this picture on the cover of *Screenplay*?" she asked him.

He nodded, not really looking, but winding the thick part of the fudge around his spoon.

"That's Jane Wyman. Well, in a year or two it's going to be Susan LaTour."

That was her stage name. She had picked the LaTour part from the paintings Dominic Centrone used to show her. They were only prints, but all the same nice to have. Her favorites were by Georges de LaTour, with the candle flames showing through people's hands the way they do in life. It also sounded like Dorothy Lamour, if she used the Bunny . . . *Dor-o-thy-La-Mour—Bun-ny-Sue-La-Tour* . . .

"Who's that?" asked Andrew.

"Come on, stonehead, you know who it is."

He shook his head and only looked at the sundae. If there was one thing bothered her, it was people looking at

their food all the time they ate. Dominic's mother used to
do that, including every fat person she could think of, including Andrew. It was like they thought some of it would
get away if they didn't keep a close watch. But she didn't
scold him, because he might get nervously upset and have
an attack right there at the Eden Reef, and she wouldn't
be able to talk to him about her career. He couldn't understand her feelings, of course, but at least he listened quietly
and sometimes even asked sensible questions. Not like Harry
or the Pappas drugstore bunch, who just thought she was
off on a toot of some kind. But why bother about them.
They'd know soon enough when she was a fantastic success and came back for a hometown visit. She would have
enough politeness to talk to them, maybe, but her attitude
would be so aloof they'd die.

"Aloof is the word I'm building my gimmick on, Andrew.
Screenplay once did an article on how all the stars with
reputations have a gimmick of some kind. Now mine is
going to be this detachment I'm working on. Not like being
sensitive or anything, but really apart from all other people
because of this mystical quality in my mind. The person
with more of this quality than anybody is Garbo. That's
why the oddball hat, which even I could wear if my face
shape was right. Things like hats and sunglasses are important. Then at the right time I fix it so my first name gets
dropped out of the lights. Impersonality that's called. Everywhere it'll read only LaTour."

She suddenly remembered there was a name on one of
Dominic's Taloose Lautrec posters. Some dancer who had
been the toast of all Paris. But she couldn't think of exactly
how it went.

Andrew was half done with his sundae and she hadn't
even started. Talking about her career always made her
absent-minded, even though she knew it was a good thing
to have an active brain. But there was a time and a place
for everything, so she concentrated on her soda—first pushing the ice cream against the side of the glass to make it

soft, then swirling it around so it was all thick and creamy.
She sucked at the top parts to get the little pieces of ice
cream still left, then drank the whole thing down in eight
long gulps. The last time it had been six. If it was beer she
would have put it away one-two-three, then had a few more
to boot. This being Sunday, though, and having Andrew
with her, there wasn't any sense thinking about beer.

"I remember," said Andrew.

"Hmmm?"

"Susan LaMour, that's your actress name."

"La*Tour*," she corrected.

He bobbed his head up and down, getting the last bits
of hot fudge out of the cup with his middle-finger tip, so it
was wrapped around the nail in a gooey bulge.

When they went outside again it was like coming out of
a movie at a different time from when you went in and not
finding anybody around. As they passed Pappas' drugstore,
though, there was still some of that coarse crowd left. Before she noticed them it was too late to cross the street
without letting them see it was deliberately to avoid them.
To make it worse, Andrew couldn't decide where he wanted
to walk, and she had to keep turning around to see where
he was while four pairs of eyes followed her every movement and looked at different parts of her body. She could
tell that.

"Hurry up, Andrew," she said, and one of the Pappas
bunch repeated it singsong with his hand on his hip.

"Hurry *up*, An*drooooo*."

When they got a little ways past, another one with his
hair all greased back and a pink sweater said, "Your leadin'
man is hanging right here, Bunny Sue."

The others laughed.

But she stayed aloof and even smiled back at them until
she was past the corner, figuring that would put them at a
loss for what to do.

They didn't have to say that about leading man hanging.
From the time she and Dominic were caught on a Formica

table in the lunch counter by Fat Herman Roach, who was the short-order cook and who should have gone home the hour before with the rest of the gang, they never let up reminding her. Dominic wanted to tear Fat Herman apart for talking about it to the Pappas bunch, and she wished now she'd let him. With Dominic it wasn't real love, not like the way it would be with a Southern Belle, but she and Dominic still knew more about each other's lives and what careers they would follow than anybody else who went together. And the part where they mixed it up wasn't disgusting like the rest, who did it anywhere, like having the girl sitting on the boy in the front seat of a car. They always took their time and found a good place, if you didn't count the one time on the table, which she remembered was cold and chilly like cold metal under her back. Dominic said it was the Fine Italian Way of doing things to take it slow. They could sit and fool around for hours, sometimes just whispering and like that before getting in. The stupid Pappas bunch called it knocking off a piece. She knew all their little ways of talking. Dominic had been so good at it, always handling himself so they were sometimes exactly on time in the end, the two of them at once. Thinking of him caused that funny tingling feeling along the inside of her legs and she felt weird about his being dead.

Just then she saw the woman in the orange sunsuit.

The woman was walking with a little girl next to her who also had on an orange sunsuit. They were dressed exactly alike, except the woman had on high-heel shoes. Andrew started to say something, but she motioned him to be quiet, since she wanted to follow without the woman's knowing about it.

"Are we playing?" whispered Andrew.

"Shhhh!"

But it was too late. The woman turned around to see who it was, and now they'd have to cross at the next corner. The man who owned the Eden Reef went by, tipping his straw summer fedora and saying, "Afternoon, Mrs. Jacoby."

Mrs. Jacoby.

For the rest of the block Bunny Sue studied her and the little girl with her. Both their waists were bare between the halters and the shorts, and the woman had a good figure. She must have been thirty. Maybe older.

Observing was the way to be. You learned about things by watching details. The woman's hair, fluffed up in a special hairdo, a touch of gray, maybe platinum, very becoming. Gray because of the hard work in being a nem-sea. Her husband maybe in Show Business too. A hard life on the road all the time.

Bunny Sue became more excited as she realized the woman might have been an actress herself and given it all up to take care of the kid. Conflicts like that happened at times.

The woman and the girl got into a little white sports car and drove away toward the exclusive part of town.

"Do you know who that was?" she asked quickly.

"Nope."

"That's a movie star. I mean, she used to be one."

"What's her name?"

"Mrs. Jacoby. Oh you wouldn't remember. It was when I was as big as you. She made musicals and love pictures."

La Goulue. That was the woman in the poster. Her hair colored orange like the sunsuits, and there was that man with the Dick Tracy nose.

"Couldn't I seen her on the TV?"

Bunny Sue didn't answer. She just walked along, fluffing her hair up on top and watching the place where she last had seen the little white car.

Their house was one of the biggest in the north part of town, if you didn't count Centrone's, which had been converted for roomers. It had distinction because her father had fixed up the front with those shingles that looked like brick. Nobody thought it was really brick, of course, but it still made a difference from a plain painted front. If her father hadn't got fat and quit taking out the fishing parties in his boat and hadn't lost the boat on account of payments, they would have had aluminum awnings and a wrought-iron stoop railing as well. Dominic and the other Centrones had lived on the first floor of the rooming house, which was stucco, but stucco was depressing. Bunny Sue had definite ideas about houses, and the best houses were made of field-stone, like the big mansions in the exclusive part of town where the woman in the orange sunsuit had gone. She would have one of those someday as a kind of other place besides her suite in New York City.

When she got inside, Andrew went over to read the funnies and her father poked his bald head over the top of the *Express*, blowing cigar smoke into the room.

"Well, Hortense," he said.

She frowned. That meant he was in a peculiar mood. Whenever he felt his oats about something he changed their names around, even calling her mom things like Lola. He went on.

"Harry says a new crowd's comin' for eats over the lunch counter."

"That nosy runt."

"He's only lookin' out for his big sister, Hortense, ha-haha . . ."

"Well, tell him to go look out a window or something." She rubbed her wrists against her hips and sat down on the floor next to the fashion section.

"Not just the lunch counter, the whole town's gettin' it," he said. "Jews and Polacks comin' for vacations."

"They only eat breakfast and snacks."

Her father set the beer can down with a peculiar grin that showed his missing tooth and said, "First wops. Now Jews and Polacks. A regular UN." He looked away nervously and coughed. Probably because he didn't mean to bring up Dominic in a way like that, but she didn't mind. "Oh well," he went on, "I used to work with all kinds down the navy yard. You don't remember the navy yard, you was too small."

"What time are we eating?" she asked.

"Ask Lola in the kitchen there. An' while you're up get me a new beer."

Jesus. He must've won a pool of some kind to get him in so peculiar a mood. Most of the time he just sat around on Sundays and brooded over that oceanfront property he wanted to buy. Then she remembered about Harry's new job and the extra money that would be coming in.

In the kitchen there was the smell of roast beef and sweet potatoes and turnips. Her mom was just getting up from bending over the stove with that worried look she always used when cooking for the whole family.

"Where'd you go with Andrew?"

"Just a walk. Over by Pappas'." She opened the refrigerator and pulled a can of Budweiser out of the six-pack, wiggling her finger over the moisture on top.

"You know he shouldn't be taking long walks, Bunny Sue. It's not good for his asthma."

The beer can splashed foam on the wall as it snapped open, and she wiped it away with the cellulose sponge: "It's a lot better than Harry marching him all over the backyard."

"At least I can keep an eye on him in the yard."

"Oh, Mom. Quit worrying."

She could still hear grumbling from the kitchen after she handed the beer to her father and turned upstairs. That was another thing she couldn't stand—women griping. You wouldn't catch her father doing that, for all his peculiar ways. Even after the fishing boat went to the bank he didn't do anything but buy a case of beer, sit down in front of the TV and say, "Well, that's that." But to hear her mom you would've thought they were out in the streets.

Upstairs in her room she stretched out on the bed and twisted her hair between her fingers. Then she stopped because she remembered it was a nervous habit and she kicked off her Wedgies, rubbing her toes together instead. It certainly was Sunday all right.

All around her on the walls were the pictures Dominic had given her or suggested she buy. Some she had framed and looking at them even now, they still made her all sad and funny inside. Especially the clowns in the diamond-design pants, which were easier to understand than the more modern types, because they had deep human qualities in them. Sometimes she was happiest doing nothing more than just this: lying on her back and looking around at those pictures. After a while it got so that nobody else seemed to be in the house or anywhere—as if she wasn't even planning to have her actress career any more.

There were also some photos of Garbo and Hedy Lamarr and some men actors hung up. She had got them by sending postcards with just the star's name and Hollywood, California, underneath. There were still a bunch of unused cards in a Russell Stover candy box in the closet that she'd never sent. They read:

> Dear ———,
> As an ardent admirer and fan of yours for many years, I would appreciate an autographed picture.
> Very Truly Yours,
> *Bunny Sue Johnson*

Then there was a space for her address, which she filled in, depending on where they lived. The photographs weren't always autographed when they came, but almost every post-card got some kind of answer. Carol Channing had sent an 8 x 10 glossy, and Ruth Roman sent a snapshot suitable for carrying in a wallet. Which she did, because that one had written *To Bunny Sue, with best wishes* across the bottom.

Thinking of postcards got letters in her head and she reached into the drawer of the night table where she kept her nylons and correspondence. She felt around with her fingers and picked up an envelope, while still lying on her back. Then she opened it and read it lazily, holding it close in front of her face.

Kimpo Airfield, Korea
17 September 1950

Dear Miss LaTour,

Well, I guess whenever you get this you'll already
know about Inchon and how everything turned out
OK. Most of the guys were really very scared because
of the tides and not knowing if it would be a surprise,
but after the rockets went in there was so much happening we didn't get scared anymore. Haha. We got
to the wrong beach which we later found it out anyhow it was a good thing because the sea wall had been
hit wide open and we just sailed in instead of using
the hook and all. I am sure all of this talk is boring
to you. Anyhow, the goons were behind the wall but
most were dead or something by the time we got
there. I think I killed a couple but that's pretty hard
to tell. The sun was going down during the landing
and the color on the burning dock and all the green
uniforms was really fabulous. Right now we are at
Kimpo which is pretty important and by the time we
get to Seoul I might become a corporal. Remember
that night on the beach with the air mattress? I think
of it so much you don't know. That was really something. Well I guess that's all for now "Bunny."

Love and Kisses

Dominic

She read the last part of the letter two times, then set it
down next to her on the chenille spread, one hand coming
to rest gently between her legs.

She supposed maybe he wasn't dead after all and that they
had made a mistake of some kind. In World War II she
heard that sometimes soldiers came walking back into
houses after everybody thought they were dead for over a
year. It was just that it was hard to think of Dominic as
frozen and buried in the same grave with all those other
Marines near some reservoir. As a matter of fact even when
she was getting the letters in the first place it wasn't like a
real war was going on. Not the same as World War II when

they had a victory garden and you listened to the radio all
the time and there was a lot of excitement in the air. With
Korea, they didn't bother much. It was a funny war.

"Bun*nyyy* . . . Bunny *Suuuuue!*"

Her mother's voice. "Would you help me in the kitchen
here?"

Oh damn, she thought. And swung her legs lazily over
the side of the bed.

"OK. In a couple of minutes."

She took off her dress and laid out a skirt and blouse to
be more comfortable, changing brassieres so she could pull
the blouse off her shoulders if she went out later. Her
father's voice rose and fell with laughter as she heard the
refrigerator door slam. While zippering up her skirt she
remembered *Gone with the Wind*, and out loud in a whisper
she said, "Don't pull so tight, Scahlett hunney. Y' gotta be
able to breathe jus' a *little* with that ol' corset."

"Bunny Suuuuue!"

"OKaaaaay!"

She put the letter back in the drawer.

For a moment she looked at it lying there with a number
of other letters and the crumpled pairs of nylons. Then she
closed the drawer and went downstairs.

It was almost an hour before dinner was on the table.
Harry came in when they were sitting down. The sweat was
pouring out of his crew cut into his face, a web belt was
holding up his fatigue pants with those big pockets on the
sides, and he was carrying the First World War rifle he had
picked up somewhere. And his arms were all dirty from
crawling around the back yard on his elbows. Maneuvers,
he called it. Just at that moment of his coming in and standing there she hated him a little. Hanging around with that
Pappas bunch didn't help his cause any, either.

"Look here, Pop," he said.

He came to attention with the gun on his shoulder, then
spun it around like a propeller and brought the butt to the
floor with a sudden thud.

"They call that With A Twirl."

"Very nice, Harry."

"Go wash your hands," said her mom. "And hurry up or the roast'll get cold."

"An' bring another beer from the kitchen, Harry."

Andrew was sitting very quiet, twisting the corners of his napkin so the middle of it made a hollow cup. She had showed him how to do that when he was only six, putting an orange in the cupped part and rolling it along the floor like it was a turtle or a crab. All this time her father was sitting still with something on his mind. She knew he was planning for one of his announcements.

Ever since losing the boat he had been thinking up plans to free them from worry later on in life and he always announced these plans at dinner, or sometimes at special meetings he called. That was the idea of property: you could always sell it for more than you paid. But she didn't understand about his special friend with oceanfront acreage. If it was available, then how come no notice in the *Express,* and how come nobody but her father knowing? But if it was true, it was a good thing for them, especially after her career began and she was out on her own.

When Harry came back in and sat down, there was a lot of sudden quiet. They all knew the announcement was coming. Her mom, especially, looked worried because it meant the roast would get colder. Then a spoon clinked on the side of a glass and Mr. Johnson cleared his throat.

"This dinner," he began, "is a special occasion. It ain't because the turnips ain't lumpy either"—he winked at Bunny Sue, but no one laughed—"it's because starting tomorrow Harry works from one o'clock and we won't eat Sunday dinners together like this no more."

That was the way he always began: saying something that was true all right, but getting the meaning so you were supposed to believe how urgent it was. Bunny Sue rubbed her nose with her napkin and looked at the wall.

"We have to appreciate," he went on, "that even though his new job is only gardening and general labor, that he works for a big important man and makes decent dough. Now that means two things." He took a quick sip of beer. "First is that this guy Jacoby is palsy with politicians and, if Harry plays his cards the way I advise, there's a chance we can wangle some kind of deal about West Point."

Andrew had been mixing a gob of butter into his sweet potatoes with a knife, but he stopped when he heard West Point. Harry was smiling and looking around. Bunny Sue heard the name and thought it to herself: *Jacoby*.

"And second, since this is extra dough coming into the house, besides what Bunny Sue gets from the lunch counter and I, uh, scrape up, we can maybe swing a down payment on that special property I've been keeping my eye on."

Harry clapped and Andrew began mixing the butter and sweet potatoes again. Her mom just sat there with that worried expression of hers. Mrs. Jacoby was the woman in the orange sunsuit. How did you like that?

Mr. Johnson took another drink from his beer, then set it down quickly as if he remembered something. "An' when I sell that property in a year, maybe two, some guy who wants to build on it right away, a Jew probably, the way they're movin' in here, he'll have to pay through the nose to get it. When you figure it up, we don't have to lay out for half of it before we got more dough back than we can use." He wiped his mouth and smiled as if he was almost through.

"We don't have it yet," said her mom.

"We will before the summer's over. Right, Harry?"

"Sure thing."

"After dinner I'll go over to the tavern and talk to this friend of mine whose property it is."

"He ain't forgot, Pop?"

"Don't be dumb, Harry. We just ain't talked business in too long. Details need discussing. Lawyers and like that."

"How much for the down payment?" asked Bunny Sue.

Her father sprinkled a little pepper on his turnips and, looking at the shaker, he said, "This friend figures a thousand."

"A *thousand* dollars?"

"Now that's less than four hundred apiece the whole summer, if I can, uh, scrape up——"

"The roast beef's getting cold," said her mom.

"Wow," said Harry. "That don't leave much for spending."

"It's an investment. The best A-1 kind of investment."

"Come on now, eat up or what's the sense of cooking a hot meal?"

There was a long pause.

"Well," said Mr. Johnson, "I wanted you to know those two important things about this dinner." He lifted his beer can for another drink, then cut a chunk of roast beef on his plate, chewing away like he was in a big hurry and had to attend to things.

It didn't look as if too much more was going to happen so Bunny Sue rubbed her nose again with the napkin and started eating. Everyone ate that way, without saying too much except to pass the butter, and when they were done she let her mom collect the plates before going in to help with the dishes.

It was later in the day, almost evening, and everything was very still. Bunny Sue was on the porch swing, looking at the pictures in her *Screenplay*. She had finished reading all the stories, which she had saved until after dinner. There was a strong smell of forsythia from the plants along the driveway. The sun was still a little hot and it was too much trouble to read the stories again so she just glanced at the captions under all the photographs. After a while her father came out and said he was going over to the tavern and talk some business. Harry had gone to Hibiscus Street to trim the hedges at the Jacoby place, and Andrew was inside watching the TV, rolling an orange inside his special napkin on the floor the way she had showed him. The sound of a window closing upstairs meant her mom was going to take a nap for her nerves.

For a long time Bunny Sue just sat on the porch that way, twisting her hair between two fingers and thinking about nothing at all except maybe the white sports car with the woman in the orange sunsuit driving, and that Taloose Lautrec poster. A couple of men turned into the street, making a lot of noise laughing together, and she turned to watch them, putting the magazine down on her lap. But when they got closer she saw that one of them was a nigger with pants like the clown painting in her room, and she felt weird. Then their laughing died off and the street became empty again.

A big bumblebee hung in the air beside the porch, and she watched it with indifference as she continued twirling her hair. It certainly was Sunday.

Dominic came back into her head and she tried to figure out what to do that night. Maybe another walk and then over to the tavern where she knew her father would buy her a beer and make jokes with her to the other men. He didn't seem to mind that once in a while. She put the *Screenplay* down on the swing and walked into the street.

She walked past Centrones', then out along the big boulevard with the sycamore trees right down the middle, then to where the real brick houses were with their gardens, and finally the fieldstone mansions set up on top of the landscaped lawns. She was saving it to ask Harry what kind of Show Business the Jacoby husband was in, for whenever he came back that night.

She was walking around that section for almost an hour, her blouse pulled down off her shoulders, which Dominic had once called full and appealing, practicing the limp she used once in a while to cause sympathy in people, when she saw the little white sports car up one of the dead-end lanes next to the low wall where the beach started.

It wasn't just the little white car that made her stop. It was Harry inside of it. It wasn't moving or anything, and after listening a while over the sound of the ocean, she realized the motor wasn't even running. But there was Harry, kneeling in the front seat it looked like, his back to her, his crew cut showing through the window. She looked up and down the street but there was no one around besides herself. As a matter of fact, she realized, the dead-end lane wasn't anywhere near Hibiscus Street where Harry's job was.

She looked up and down again, then tiptoed into the lane to see what was going on. He still hadn't seen her by the time she got up even with the car. Then she saw something very crazy. Next to Harry, lying down across the driver's seat, was the woman in the orange sunsuit. Her halter was pulled over so that one breast was partially exposed and Harry had a hand on her little orange pants.

Bunny Sue Johnson stood there and looked at them in the front seat of the white sports car and then screamed at the top of her lungs.

"You disgusting filthy animal, Harry!"

The figures in the car jumped apart with a shock.

"You disgusting filthy pig!"

She stood there looking at the both of them, her head stuck forward, the tiny veins coming out purple and blue on her temples, the woman in the orange sunsuit pulling the halter back over her breast and Harry staring at her in horror.

"Get out of here," he said, trembling.

She stood there screaming at them as loud as she could, with the growing feeling in her stomach that she was going to throw up all over the place.

THE PRIEST THAT FROM THE ALTAR BURST

Dick had spent some time in school with Jesuit preachers. And that left a deep impression. I don't know how to describe it: I was in a Catholic convent for one year when I was five and it left me with such a feeling of being watched by the Great-Somebody-Up-There—just a spooky and eerie feeling. I think Dick and I shared that same feeling.

M.F.

The priest that from the altar burst
To brimstoned hatred of life's lust
Had face burned red by wind and wine
With hair blown wild by an unknown blast.

He lived beyond the parish wall
And feeble women with their shawls
Would shuffle past with heads bowed low
And never hear the roars within.

And as the mass would suffer on
In dormant drama of that day
When blood burned forth and He cried out
Father Forgive Them, My Father Forgive Them.

The priest that from the altar burst
Would tear the vestments from his back
And throw them down in saddened heap
Where it said Sanctus, Sanctus, Sanctus.

THE VISION
OF
BROTHER FRANCIS

Here's the Jesuit thing again. I think that's where Dick's demons began. He said that through centuries and centuries of art, demons kept turning up in paintings and sculptures and they all had something similar about them. You could always recognize a demon. They all had the same kind of features. And, therefore, said Dick, demons certainly must exist somewhere. And I'm sure he believed it.

M.F.

. . . but, (O my shining stars and body!) how hath
fanespanned most high heaven the skysign of soft
advertisement. But was iz? Iseut? Ere were sewers?
The oaks of ald now they lie in peat yet elms leap
where askes lay. Phall if you but will, rise you must:
and none so soon either shall the phrace for the
nunce come to a setdown secular phoenish.

Finnegans Wake

With faceless demons squatting in the corners of his
room (before the tinkling swish of Harlem's lights
had blotted from his mind the Virgin's bells and silks), how
many times had Matthew Corr—Brother Francis then,
balding, alone and quiet with the seven seals—thought back
along the six mute years to the glorious day of his call? How
many times had he seen himself standing on the Massachusetts hill, high in the patch of thick-smelling weeds when
that wind had dropped from the late summer sky to roar
and howl in the trees (youth flecking away like plaster
pages from an aging wall)? Only for him, he knew, had
that wind come washing back the desires of other years,
pounding violently in the air about him. Then on away so
that (yes) he knew finally it was God whose great numb
fingers pressed against his soul, a mute amoeba-like thing,
translucent and veined.

He had seen out across the valley to the other hills
beyond, tracing their shape and form as they lumped off
into the rippling horizon. The skyline was a misty blue and
the wind had paused and taken breath, the sun had vanished into a canyon of opaque clouds, and the very air had
seemed to shudder in his ears. With tears stinging the roots
of his eyes he felt he had been given a sign. That this would
be the way of his life: the hills that rose from the far side

of a valley; a valley that vanished in color and smoke.
This was himself. And it was God; and it was the way of
his serving God, and once and forever it was his call.

Before that night in Harlem (the pulpy flesh of the
woman's belly beneath his hand), he had thought many
times of the Postulancy with its complex rite and dogma
that seemed not at all in keeping with the promise of his
wind on the hill. He saw again the slender impeccable
fingers of the monsignor sitting before him, the single line
of dissatisfaction etched in a flawless curve on his brow
as he shook his reproving head from side to side. And he
remembered their combined reasoning, that if he were to
continue at all in the service of God he should give up the
priesthood and go to the novitiate in Lowell. The responsibilities of the priest, the details and confusions implicit in
the day-to-day duties of sacerdotal life were simply not
what he had been led to believe. He would go instead to
Lowell, become a Xavierian brother, and teach in gram-
mar schools rather than say the mass. He could then imagine
(and later could remember) no isolated factor, no single
reason for deciding to leave the Postulancy. It seemed that
like the wind, which had fallen at Another's whim, the
decision was part of a multifaceted force beyond his own
reason; that this force would guide and compel him through
life, visiting and revisiting in the hours of need, making
him the object of continuing revelations. Thoughts of com-
petence and ability, even when the monsignor had insisted
he hasten the decision to leave, never entered his mind. His
only reflection was that God had strange ways. He could
not become a priest.

Now and again he remembered the pleasant countryside
of Lowell where the afternoons were spent in quiet dis-
cussions and occasional games of softball, where the im-
plications of his duties were far less staggering to the senses,
and where he nonetheless was swept with regret that he
would go through life without the power of Holy Orders.
It might have been nice, after all, to be able to turn from
the veiled tabernacle (*his* fingers there in the most secret

hiding place of God), to bless the congregation of bowed, respectful heads. It would be his own hand then, the nails as pared and even as he remembered all priests' were, moving through the air in graceful benediction, the sacramental words visited upon him, his arm pulsing with the wonder of transubstantiation: *In Nomine Patris et Filii et Spiritus*— but it could never be. The other complexities would of necessity have entered into his life as well: praying over the bloated dead, hearing the confessions of women, and what if he made some mistake such as dropping the Eucharist during the mass (always clumsy and fumbling), would it dissolve into blood there on the marble of the altar? Where had he heard that? And the little boy who never swallowed the hosts but who stored them in a barrel until it was full and one day he lifted the lid to find they all had turned into wine. No, it was better this way, with the simple, unadorned life of quiet teaching before him. Brother Francis—he liked the name. His boys would love their Brother Francis.

II

There had been the drab overcrowded school in Brooklyn: the separate buildings for the boys and girls with narrow concrete yards for punchball and other recess games. The buildings were square or rectangular, covered with a veneer of gray stucco and set off only by the foreboding Gothic of the church itself; the grim incense-smelling court which he could see from the single window in his room, where the parish priests strolled, muttering their offices to themselves, and the acolytes gathered in affected silence before high mass. He found in each day (remembering the one before as ages gone and knowing how still later he would look back and see them all as if in another time, in someone else's life) the growing need to know why God had so sent that wind, had chosen him from others to do . . . he was not sure just what. This Brooklyn school, its

name of The Sacred Heart celebrated in faded Tintoretto-
like paintings on the ceiling of the church, had no winds
for him nor any grass nearby where he could stroll about,
half expecting a breeze, a muted echo of his call. There
was only the gray of stucco and cement, the depressing
chalked boundaries of games, and the trolley cars that
rattled and clanged the avenue along which the school
buildings sat. Even the people who went to mass each
morning, shuffling down the long aisles like crabs, were
gray and depressing. It pained him to hear their crude
whispered speech, their hypocritical respect for the unknown. Many of them left just after the gospel, staying
only long enough to fulfill the obligation, dipping their
dirty fingers into the holy-water fonts as they went (the
sacramental afterthought, apology for insult). But he knew
their type, especially the women, so what did it matter?
Fat, heavy things with dresses showing dark stains under
the armpits, only good for boiling their husband's dinner
or raising young boys to serve God. Sometimes he hated
the women. Whenever he watched them kneeling, with their
buttocks resting on the pews, or moving off in small awed
groups to receive communion (little flowered handkerchiefs
on their heads, self-indulgent piousness), he despised them.
Vacant heads sensing fear, he would think, What do they
love as they pray? Some incense-smell called God. Or whatever. They never had a wind. Still, some of them were
probably devout enough. But when he saw their rayon
dresses clinging to their heavy legs in the heat, the loose
unbridled fat hanging beneath their biceps, he was glad to
be sitting away by himself in the side aisle reserved for the
clergy, his starched Roman collar gently chafing his neck.
No one to bother with, he would think. A holy man. Let
him sit alone.

He sat one Friday afternoon after Benediction, content
in the quiet warmth of the church, when a growing un-
easiness made him aware of someone's presence. The sun

had just vanished behind the low afternoon clouds, plunging the already dark pews into somber gloom as the last dirge-like chords of the "Tantum Ergo" still hovered in the high beams and arches of the church. He turned and looked behind him, but the rows were all empty. There was nothing save the colloidal dust raised by the now-departed congregation. Yet the feeling of another presence persisted and he moved uneasily away from his position under the relief figures carved on the station of the cross. The sharp crack and echo of a warping board caused him to start quickly, and when he closed his eyes for an instant, he became aware of a veiled figure that was appearing gradually and without warning on the glowing red of his eyelids. He blinked quickly and strained to make out her features, but she was further away now, in the distance, it seemed, back at the extreme limits of consciousness where only the flickering half-light of perception gave her any substance or form. And the darkness at her back seemed the very abyss of eternity. She was thin and without real dimension, hardly more than the echo of a shade, but somehow recognizable. And now she moved. Was it toward him? He squeezed his eyes tightly and strained to see her more clearly, but his energy was draining and he sensed the encroaching evil of temptation. Wanting and not wanting to see more, the sensation of evil pressing upon him, almost physiological, he opened his eyes widely, thought of his wind, and drove the vision from his mind. Under his breath he murmured *Beata Maria semper Virgini* . . . and he sat for some stunned moments in the empty church that still smelled of incense from the service, where the dust was suspended in the barely discernible shafts of gloomy light.

III

Sitting at the heavy wooden desk with the alphabet inscribed in long sheets of black cardboard above the slate panels at his back, Brother Francis conducted his classes at The Sacred Heart and referred to himself only in the third person.

"Brother Francis," he would say, "will give a test to-morrow in the geography of the Middle Atlantic States."

He would say this only after his boys had just returned to class: after morning prayers, or recess, or occasionally just after lunch when the inertia from outside concerns was running down in their minds and they began waiting in twos and threes for the word or specific instruction that would shape the activity of the remaining school hours. Then when the class was perfectly quiet and each head was focused on his desk—bare except for a single bottle of ink and an old straight pen—he would make his various an-nouncements. There were always little sounds of dismay, and mumbling, but the sudden forward thrust of his head and the sweep of his ready-to-accuse eyes were always too effective for any continuing protest. He would trail the tips of his fingers scratchily along the starched Roman collar (white, he remembered, for purity) and think of how good his boys were after all. In the tradition of the school, always thought of as disciplined and more than a little firm, they came to classes well scrubbed and clean. The Xavierian Brothers, he knew, were well respected in the neighborhood; they were said to temper firmness with just the proper amount of generosity and patience in their treatment of the children. And the parents felt secure (their preoccupations elsewhere) that their sons were being shaped through their formative years by such good men. Believing himself to be such a man and to be continually reflecting the established traditions of the order and the school, Brother Francis ac-cepted and enjoyed their trust.

Still, his mind had become clouded with temptation and evil. Why had that vision come? After the Friday afternoon in the church, he spent hours thinking about what might have caused it and trying to remember just when it was (years, perhaps) that he had experienced the same thing before. It was in the way she moved—that motion of her hips—but each time he was close, he lost it and the memory of the single, more recent vision obscured from his consciousness any connections in another time. He only knew that if ever it came again he must respond by thinking of his wind on the day of the call, or how the freshly cut grass had smelled after the spring rains in Lowell. That was the way he had dispatched his fear as a boy, lying in bed and watching the form of his father's overcoat as it hung from the bedroom door changing shape in the darkness and looming up with demons ready to spill out the sleeves; and he would think of Santa Claus or the dollhouse he had always wanted secretly, until the thoughts were so good that when he opened his eyes again, there was the coat hanging properly on the door and his mind was unclouded and free. His mind. What if the parents of his boys could see into his mind? Or the people who sat across from him on the trolley cars, or anybody, for that matter? At times, sitting with the other brothers at the large oval-shaped dinner tables, he would feel a pair of eyes on his face and his blood would rise in the fear that his thoughts, his vision, were known—that others could see into his mind and know each guarded thought, even the secret pleasure that he sometimes had in the warm shower. Then he would touch his collar nervously with the tips of his fingers and smile. He would say to himself the words of the *Confiteor* and trail his nails slowly along the starched collar from just under the ear to his chin. Clean nails they were, well pared and even, with the cuticles carefully trimmed.

But the vision came again. And still again, hovering for a moment on a distant, almost impossibly remote aspect of his consciousness, dangerous, delicious, so that even thoughts of his wind would not drive it away and he allowed it to remain. But then the gestures of the Virgin (he knew her now), the vague obscenity of her motions, would weaken him and he would go to his room, drugged, a little dizzy, and open to the revelation of St. John. The vision only came after sundown then, and he would turn on the little wall lamp, removing the shade so that the shadows

were angled, hard, and sharp in the room. He read that
way sometimes for hours, alone in the small wicker chair
under the shadeless bulb thinking of St. Francis, his
namesake, and the Giotto painting which showed him
preaching to birds. There was another painting too (whose
was that?), where he stood at the mouth of a cave, his
arms extended in supplication and his desk within the cave,
a skull and an open book resting on its top. Ascetic was the
word for that. Brother Francis, the ascetic saint. But whose
painting? No matter, really. He would sit that way, reading,
looking up every so often and over at the narrow bed with
the taut black quilt, and the crucifix arranged on the pillow, being remotely aware of the mind that had made the
words before him, words that seared into his brain until
their force became a motion, a direction, and it was no
longer necessary to read, only to stare up at the burning
bulb and let the intangible inertia carry him along, the
terror of the seven seals engulfing his soul (translucent
amoeba, veined and glowing). Staring that way, his pupils
shrunk to pinpoints from exposure to the bulb, it seemed
to him that he no longer wore the black habit of the
Xavierians. Now, his skull was shaven on top and he had
grown a beard. Somewhere the sparrows and wrens were
waiting in the trees for him to come to the woods, his bare
feet padding on the forest floor, his arm and hand raised
in benediction. He would gesture delicately with his fingers
and the birds would leave the trees, fluttering through the
air about his head as he leaned over to preach gentle words
to those already settling on the ground. My children, he
thought; My clean and lovely children.

IV

For Brother Francis, the years at The Sacred Heart passed
slowly and heavily. He saw the first class that he had taught,
the fifth grade, graduate and pass off into a different life,
their faces changed somewhat, their voices deepening and

breaking with adolescence. Lay teachers were hired as the enrollment of the school increased and a few of the other Xavierians were transferred to different schools. There came times when he would rise from his bed in the morning (sleep a peculiarly half-conscious condition then; later, almost nonexistent) and look into his little mirror for a long time before adjusting his habit, and step into the hallway as if he had just turned from an open grave to go back to the cares of daily life. His patience grew quick and inconstant and sometimes his ability to endure even the smallest collective duty was challenged. Retreats, for instance, or anything that involved affiliated form and order. Perhaps if he had become a monk instead—a room off to himself where no one came, a cave with moist walls that was dark and warm . . .

He took to testing his boys through entire afternoons so he could doze at his desk and meditate quietly on some of the notions that haunted him most often. Still, there was some consolation in being with the boys and it was certainly better than having to say mass for small groups of sweating women in thick-heeled shoes. The boys were bright and clean. Many times he would sit and think of them as if they were a great way off instead of there in the rows before him, with their pencils moving noiselessly on their notebooks; and he would imagine their clean arms and legs, the cool unspoiled flesh of their slender bodies. Now and again he fashioned himself the gentle saint, and he walked through the aisles placing his hand on the backs of their necks or their wrists, causing them to stop for a moment and gaze up at him. With love in their eyes, he thought (and later remembered).

Sometimes in the evenings he would put on his street clothes and take long walks through Brooklyn. It was warmer in the evenings then, but without a wind, and the heat hung heavily in the evening air. As he walked, he would look at each thing that passed him by: the long rows of granite and sandstone buildings, gray and oppressive; the women too, as they stared out of their windows with elbows propped on the sills, watching the people below or the windows on the opposite side of the street or nothing at all. Sudden waves of nausea would sweep through him whenever he looked up and thought of their fleshy arms and legs. How did their husbands ever bring themselves— But that was something he must keep himself from thinking.

During one of these evenings (a cooler evening than the others, the air with a hint of autumn blowing) he felt a familiar stirring in his blood, a desire to have again something that once had happened. But he did not know what it was. For almost an hour as he walked along, he tried to fix this other place, this time, in his mind. But it remained out of the grasp of his apprehension and he became content with nothing but the feeling of nostalgia itself. It was almost a pleasant sensation, sad, yes, but still with a hint of sweetness, and he felt he must not let it get away. He must complement the tender pain.

The only sounds in the street were distant: a child yelling, a mother calling, the clunk of a manhole cover as the wheels of an automobile ran it over. He glanced around him, then stepped easily into the first tavern he came across and ordered a beer. It was a strange place, smelly and full of noise, but it was a good distance from The Sacred Heart and he would not be known.

"Draft or bottle?" asked the bartender.

"A draft would be fine."

The bartender placed a tapered glass under the tap and drew off the beer, allowing some of the foam to flow over the top, then leveling it away with a plastic stick.

"There y' go."

"Thank you."

As he put the glass to his lips, he felt the eyes of some of the other men on his back and he swallowed the beer slowly, looking down into the glass as it emptied. It was cold and soothing after the brief walk. What if they knew, those men? But that was silly. (How could they if he was wearing street clothes?) Although some said it was always possible to tell a man of God no matter how he dressed.

Remember the communist purges and how they always found the priests? But what if they knew his thoughts as well? He set the glass on the bar and without shifting his eyes from his image in the gilded mirror ordered another, this time with rye.

"What kind y' want?"

"Pardon me?"

"What kinda whiskey?"

"Oh no, that doesn't make any difference."

"Seagram's all right?"

"Yes, that's fine."

Now he was sure of the eyes watching him and he drank the rye quickly, following it with long lumps of beer. He took a deep breath when he had done and closed his eyes for a moment, allowing the strength of the alcohol to spread along his limbs, tingling and warming the nerves and bringing to his mind a faint, delicate hummm.

Yes, he thought, that was much better now. The edges were dulled and softened. For no immediate reason tears welled up in his eyes and he remembered the nostalgia of just a few minutes before. It was good to have sadness (ephemeral crosses to bear). The other men in the bar were laughing at something that had just happened in the game of shuffleboard and he turned to watch them. A hand sprinkling resin on the surface of the wood, the sliding weight, the tilted glasses of beer while the scores were rung up. These things were occurring but they had no meaning. He observed them absently and without commitment of any kind.

There was music coming from the jukebox, a slow shuffling kind of song that crept rhythmically into his mind and suggested the movement in his vision. Slowly now, deliberately, he leaned his head back and narrowed his eyes into slits so that the barroom became a blur of colors and lights, a phantasmagoric distortion of shapes.

She was there again, the Virgin, moving slowly to the pulsing rhythm of the music, swaying easily, oriental gauzes and silks draped from her shoulders and bosom.

"You all right, buddy?"

He started.

"What?"

The bartender was watching him and drying a glass with a white towel.

"You want another drink?"

"Oh. No, no thank you. That's fine. How much is that?"

"Sixty-five."

He took a dollar from his wallet and placed it on the bar, in a small puddle of beer.

"Oh, I'm sorry," he said.

The bartender lifted the wet bill and said nothing.

"You can keep the change."

The bartender nodded without speaking and Brother Francis turned and walked unsteadily toward the door. The voices surged in laughter behind him, filling his ears with their echo, mixing and flooding with the music from the jukebox, which seemed to be growing louder, increasing the speed of its rhythm, and piercing the air with shrieks and noises. He hesitated a moment at the door, hovered there waiting for something to occur, a wind perhaps, a sound . . . But nothing came.

Then he stepped out into the night, the sounds ceasing abruptly behind him, and he walked on, not caring where, a distant hum echoing in his brain.

V

He was wary of the bars after that, wanting (but trying to avoid) the lovely warm feeling of the liquor in his body, helping his sadness and easing the vision into his mind.

The Virgin. He must be terribly careful now. He was a chaste and good man who had sworn a vow of chastity. There was the whiteness of his Roman collar and the slender unspoiled bodies of his boys. So like the birds that waited for him to come. So unlike the women.

Sitting at his desk by the blackboard with his face

propped on one hand and half watching the pencils move in the rows before him, he felt the heat of the sun on his cheek and remembered his stepsister in Massachusetts when he was thirteen. There had been that same warmth over his whole body then, even through the clothes, and hers as well. But what was her name? Strange to forget that. She had lain beside him on the grass, talking a kind of nonsense until she twisted over once so that her skirt shifted up over her knees. He remembered the surge of unknown weakness in his bowels when he saw her thighs, wanting suddenly to place his hands upon them and, yes, he remembered something more—he wanted his cheek against them, kissing the flesh and rubbing it with his own. What made him want that? The feeling had left him weak. But the girl had seen his eyes and would not pull her skirt back down. Instead, she moved nearer and let her legs touch his. She tore up some grass and threw it at him. Then she placed her hands on his chest.

"Trust me?" she asked.

It was a game his friends had talked of. Should he play?

"Do you trust me?" she asked again.

He was silent and confused by the drawing feeling in his bowels. What was causing that?

"Are you scared?" she asked.

"No."

"Yes, you are. You're afraid."

"I'm not."

"You'd have to confess it and the priest would make you kneel down in front of the church."

"No," he said. His face was flushed with humiliation.

"Then," she said, moving her fingers slowly over his shoulders, "do you trust me?"

He closed his eyes and nodded, slowly at first, then quickly.

She asked again—this time her hands on his hips.

"No," he said.

"Silly. Then it's your turn."

He tried her shoulders and she answered yes. Then her

rib cage and hips, each time receiving the same answer and a small laugh. She continued to laugh, and gradually his confusion and humiliation were changing to rage. But he could not stop. All at once he reached out and put both hands on her bare thighs. She squirmed slightly and with the vaguest deliberation, moved her legs apart.

"Yes," she said.

He stopped.

"Go on. I trust you." And she laughed.

He was unable to move, his temples throbbing and his entire body pulsing with a rhythm, strange and unknown.

"You're afraid," she said. "You'd have to go and confess." She laughed and moved her fingers to his belly. He shrank back but could not take his hands from her thighs.

"Aren't you?" she asked. And she dropped a hand quickly between his legs, held it still for a moment, then squeezed and pressed gently with her fingers.

"Say a prayer if you're afraid," she said. She moved against him so that their legs pressed together and she kept her hand between his legs, squeezing softly. "Say an Our Father and a Hail Mary." He pressed back, somehow understanding the rhythm of her hand, and he swayed easily, his eyes half closed. "Say the stations of the cross. Say the rosary."

"Brother Francis."

The name darted into his mind and he jumped awake at the desk, making a little sound of fear in his throat.

"May I be excused, Brother Francis?"

The boy was in the third row with his hand in the air.

"May I please be excused?"

VI

He felt now that his wind was lost to him forever. It was a way God had of punishing him for his sins—not such bad sins after all, compared with the slime that seethed in other people's lives, but then how hideous they must have

seemed to God when they stained and tainted a soul that
had been so white. But that was the Way of God, and he
must never question it. And perhaps it was a test, this keeping away of his wind (the most beautiful and roaring of
winds, choked back into the sky, never to swing down
away from the hills and breathe the surging power of love
on his body). Now he had only his boys and his readings
at night with the shadeless bulb flinging sharp patterns on
the wall. A symbol of poverty, his vow. And each evening
as he read, he drank a small glass of blackberry brandy. He
had found a Jewish neighborhood in Rugby where there
was no danger of being known, and sandwiched between a
chicken market and dry-goods store was a small liquor
shop, the prices printed in iridescent colors on the window.
He had told the man he needed something for a cold (the
fall was here, and it might be a good idea to have something
around in case of cold . . .). Blackberry brandy, the man
had told him, was just the thing for that. So each evening
he read—it was Solomon now—and he sipped from a small
glass filled with the pleasing, heavily textured liquor.

> Depart from the peak of Ama'na,
>> from the peak of Senir and Hermon,
> from the dens of lions,
>> from the mountains of leopards.
> You have ravished my heart,
>> my sister, my bride,
> You have ravished my heart
>> with a glance of your eyes . . .
> I arose to open to my beloved,
>> and my hands dripped with myrrh,
> my fingers with liquid myrrh,
>> upon the handles of the bolt.
> I opened to my beloved,
>> but my beloved had turned and gone.
> My soul failed me when he spoke.
>> I sought him, but found him not;
> I called him, but he gave no answer . . .

Yes, he thought, yes. Yes. There was something in all
that. He nodded to himself one evening, finishing the passage, and enjoyed the warm feeling that the brandy lent to

his cheeks. He leaned back in his chair, half closing his eyes, and thought of Solomon, and of caravans inching humpbacked across the desert, Sheba approaching the land of the Jews.

And the vision came again, gently this time, emerging from a field of pastel shapes, amorphous and ephemeral. The Virgin, there in robes—no, they were silks and gauzes of pink and yellow. They blew (it seemed they blew in a stirring breeze) as she swayed easily from side to side. Was she beckoning now? He stood from the chair with his eyes still half closed, his head back, and he walked over to the bed where he sat, then reclined on the black quilt, holding the vision securely in his mind, refusing now to let it go. Sounds began, beads and tinkling bells (and he listened to them), these sounds that rose and fell as she placed each slippered foot ahead of her on the ground. And yes, there was a smell—a dull narcotic incense that came to drug his brain. She swayed closer, and closer still so that he could almost make out the features of her face and he watched her fingers caressing the air, following the gestures of the dance. Hail Mary, he said aloud, Full of grace— He stopped as something touched his leg, and he opened his eyes quickly to find his own hand crawling slowly along his thigh.

VII

It was late fall when he began his walks in other sections of the city. The novelty of having new students (learning their names, their preoccupations and habits) had begun wearing off and he was settling into a kind of predictable day-to-dayness that had no reward save the pleasure of the warm shower he promised himself each evening, and put off until as late as possible.

But to spend the earlier portions of the evenings reading and meditating in his room was becoming more difficult.

Because now Brother Francis felt he was not alone during the times when the vision did not come. There were faceless demons squatting in the corners of his room, leering and waiting . . . He had yet to lift his eyes and stare back at them, but he knew they were there. (Remember Luther, he would think, throwing the bottle of ink at the specter of Satan that came to tempt him. The splotch on the wall still there for all to see.)

Mostly he knew the demons from their heavy oppressive smell, almost a sexual odor tinged with ammonia and hinting of evil. But to not look at them (to know they were there and not to look) was defying that evil. Still, he became afraid whenever the room was empty, and suddenly their presence would come swooping from nowhere, carrying a sinking weight to his chest. Then he felt his defiance was not enough and that before long they might creep over from the corners of the room to wrap their scaly arms and legs about his own and press their mouths against his flesh. Whenever this feeling came upon him, he would dress quickly and escape out into the street.

And yet that too became less and less of an answer: the depressing repetition of the Brooklyn architecture, and the static dullness of the neighborhood faces having their only synthesis in boredom. He needed lights of a kind, brighter colors and people moving about him, with someplace of their own to go (who were not simply propped into a window frame gazing themselves through time).

At first when he abandoned Brooklyn, he left the rectory wearing his habit so that the other brothers would say nothing—there had been times when he sensed murmurings against him, vague sounds of suspicion and mistrust. But after locating the new sections and areas that suited him best, he would change into street clothes, swallow two or three glasses of brandy, and revisit their streets in the night. He purchased three Hawaiian shirts with red and yellow flowers painted on the front and back, and he wore them each in turn out over his trousers so that his belly (bloating now, and expanding with the years) would not be so conspicuous.

Times Square was an initial favorite. He loved to watch the people hurrying along: young girls and sailors, boys (not so different from his own), and strange, intensely expressioned people who wore sunglasses in the night. But on one occasion he went into a movie house on Forty-second Street, and sat next to a woman smelling of perspiration and drinking wine through a straw from a Coca-Cola bottle. After that, the section was spoiled for him and he did not go back.

For a while then, he tried Queens, but no matter what part he chose, it was almost as bad as Brooklyn (small factories, projects, the land of the dead and dying), and eventually he settled on Manhattan. The Plaza at Central Park with its flowers and hansom cabs, and the statue of Prometheus at Radio City became his two favorite places. The people who walked through these areas were well dressed and moved with a kind of purpose and determination. He could never imagine them sitting up in some cheap wallpapered apartment in their underwear, drinking beer from cans and watching television. He could not really think of them as doing anything but walking busily past fountains and gilded statues, smiling at one another, perhaps pausing for a moment to look at the tinkling splash of the water.

But Harlem was an accident. He had not planned to do anything but ride uptown on the West Side local, then walk across Central Park South to the Plaza. But he had fallen asleep for what seemed only an instant, then jumped awake as the train lurched into 125th Street. He stumbled quickly out onto the platform, rubbing his eyes and looking around curiously for a familiar sign or perhaps an indication that it was some kind of mistake about to be rectified with no effort on his part. But as the train pulled away behind him, and the faces of the Negroes and Puerto Ricans became established in his mind, he was swept with the impulse to go up into the strange streets instead of just crossing the platform for the downtown train.

The evening was warm, without a breeze of any kind, and after strolling for a short while he became disappointed. The buildings, though taller, had much the same grayness and lack of character that had driven him from Brooklyn. Yet there was something more that he noticed: a kind of subdued, almost tense excitement in the great number of people who roamed about, in the women who smiled occasionally at him (what for? a deliberate thought-out smile) as he passed them by. A quality in these women caused a distant stirring in his loins—a feeling that he remembered from another time and place. It was the slight hint their hips gave the air, a kind of easy swaying that reminded him somehow—but no, that was foolish to even think. There could be no connection. Still . . .

He stayed home the following week and attempted to read. It was a conscious effort, almost a calculated diversion from whatever it was that kept Harlem in his mind. He was wary, even apprehensive, of returning there, as if something, someone, were waiting for him in the populated streets.

He sat and forced his attention on the pages of the Bible before him, keeping his eyes away from the leather-skinned creatures that clawed the floor in the corners of his room (waiting too, knowing, their hideous leer a betrayal of intent). He read and forced himself to remain in the room, not going out at all except for classes and meals and setting seven days as the limit of his abstinence from wandering. Wandering. He liked the word. Ishmael and Hagar. Forty days and forty nights. Caravans slouching across the desert.

At the end of the seventh day, Brother Francis put on the favorite of his three Hawaiian shirts, buffed his shoes, and extinguished the shadeless bulb in his room. While standing there quietly, about to turn, he sensed one of the demons ready to spring and he dove for the door, pulling it shut behind him just as the hideous thing would have

fallen on his chest and throat. The slamming door echoed
through the rectory halls and he jumped down the stairs
two at a time, never bothering to look behind him and
hearing only the scratching sounds of an animal on the
door inside his room.

When he reached the street he took a series of long
breaths and rubbed his hands over his heavy chest to soothe
the heart that pounded and fluttered (it seemed to him)
like some kind of enraged bird. There was a gentle breeze
beginning, and he walked along slowly, then quickly toward
the subway station as a trolley car clanged along under the
rows of Brooklyn windows, where any number of women
sat, with their elbows propped on the sills, to watch the
evening.

This was a Friday and as soon as he reached Harlem,
Brother Francis felt an even greater surge of excitement
than he had known the week before. All over the streets
people gathered in small groups on benches or stoops, or
walked easily here and there, talking to one another and
laughing over some secret they all seemed to share.

Just east of Broadway he passed a number of Negroes,
all tall and thin, gathered around two men in polo shirts
who sat on a railing and thumped lazily on a pair of bongo
drums. Some of the young people were dancing, their
bodies pressed tightly together, their feet rising and falling
to the slow pulsing rhythm of the drums. He watched them
for some moments in stunned silence until a piercing voice
made itself heard in his ears and he realized he had been
hearing it for some time.

"It ain' right," the voice was yelling.

Brother Francis turned and saw a man at the edge of a
small square, standing on a crate and gesturing at a crowd
of almost twenty people. With one more glance at the dancing couples (their legs rising and falling together), he
turned toward the square to listen to the speaker whose

voice now barely carried over the sound of traffic and people.

". . . been gettin' it in South Carolina," he was saying, "but *we* been sittin' still an' still get their heel grine in our face an' I stan' here to tell you all it ain' right!"

"It ain' right," murmured the crowd, an echo, their heads nodding lazily. One of them turned and stared in his direction. And Brother Francis, seeing the expression in his eyes, suddenly understood the speaker's subject and felt his stomach heave in fear.

Something touched him on the shoulder and he heard a male voice ask, "How y' doin'?"

It was a tall, pink-hatted Negro, smiling so that all of his teeth showed.

"I beg your pardon?" said Brother Francis.

"I jus' say how you doin'?" The words were singsong, almost melodic, and this time the man spoke with his head cocked to one side. He was wearing a powder-blue suit, and both hands were in the jacket pockets. Brother Francis grinned back uneasily, his voice quivering.

"I'm fine," he said.

"Why, tha's good, man. Not enough people 'round nowadays fine's they should be, you know what I mean? You jus' out for a little walk in the evenin' air?"

"It's a nice evening, yes," said Brother Francis. His hands were clammy with perspiration and he wiped the palms along the lower part of his flowered shirt and looked around him. No one seemed to be paying them any attention, but he could not escape the feeling of being watched.

"Shame you-all alone though. Things maybe a lil' quiet in your part a' town?"

"A little, yes."

"I know what you mean. Gets lonely sometimes where there's no kind a' scenes goin' on. You up here for a little entertainment?"

"Well, sometimes I walk around of an eve . . ."

The Negro's smile grew broader, he looked once over each shoulder, then patted Brother Francis on the shoulder, leading him away from the sidewalk and over next to the storefronts.

"Man, I know *exactly* what you mean. You lookin' for a little somethin' put fun in you evenin's. I got jus' the thing."

He moved Brother Francis nearer the corner so they could both see the row of benches that lined the small park and which had been obscured by the speaker and the crowd.

". . . takin' it in Georgia and Tennessee, but it ain' right to be takin' here . . ."

"You see them little honeys on the en' bench over there?" asked the Negro.

Brother Francis looked at him nervously, then followed the gesture to the last of the benches where three Negro girls were sitting and talking to each other. Each of them was wearing a different-colored satin dress, and their legs were crossed so that the hems were up over their knees. His mind fumbled for an instant over the legs he remembered from somewhere else. *Say a prayer if you're afraid . . .*

"Them three's mine, man, an' it's still pretty early in the evenin', so you get a choice."

Say the stations of the cross. Say the rosary.

"Course, if you like a real honey roll, you'd take Myrna on the right there. You know what I mean?"

Brother Francis turned his gaze from the three girls talking on the bench to the leering face of the Negro in front of him. With fear and fascination he looked at the eyes and teeth, and a little smile began weakly, uncontrollably at the corners of his mouth. He took a step backward, still staring at the face, then another until there was more than six feet between himself and the other man. He again wiped his hands along his shirt ends, then turned and walked away with quick nervous steps, looking continually behind him.

"Where you goin', man?" asked the Negro. "Don' you like my girls? Don' you like Myrna on the right there?"

". . . got no reason t'put us down like it was someplace else and not right here. It jus' ain' right . . ."

He ran the last few steps to the corner, still glancing around and feeling the eyes of some of the crowd on his back as he went. When he reached the next street he put his fingers nervously up to his Roman collar, then stopped dead as he realized he was not wearing it. For a moment he felt lost and alone; and he could see in his mind's eye a barren wind-swept plain where a thick-winged bird of prey hovered in lazy circles over his body as he crawled and stumbled along the ground.

The sudden honking of horns jarred the image out of his consciousness, and he thought again of the man's face, the pink, narrow-brimmed hat. Whose loins spilled him out? Foul and evil thing that he was; child of wrath. And those three women. Mary on the right there. But my God, her legs . . .

The street he turned into was quieter than the square, and he walked along in silence, seeing little and hearing the sounds of traffic and voices as if they were off in another world somewhere. He wondered about the stockings of the women, how far they went up under the dresses, and about the place where they ended and the flesh began. Was it softer there or what was it like? Somewhere a hymn was being sung and as he moved on, its sound grew louder and more sustained than the others he had been hearing. Across on the opposite side of the street he could see the people singing in the second story of a building. He crossed over without thinking, then backed away to look up again. DADDY HAPPINESS, said the sign. Faded letters on a piece of board. There was organ music too, he could hear it now under the cacophony of voices, but it was impossible to distinguish either melody or words. The voices pierced each other and fell together, seeming only to possess the essential force and direction of the song. He listened for a few moments, looked back up the street from which he had just come, then entered and began climbing stairs without giving it thought except at the precise moment of its happening. The stairs were wooden and creaked under his weight as he reached the second landing. There was still another sign over the door: CONGREGATIONAL CHURCH OF DADDY HAPPINESS. YOU ARE WELCOME.

An old man in a soiled blue suit and without teeth nodded to him when he passed over the threshold, and indicated a seat in the rear as the singing continued. Most of the congregation were women, and they moved their heads from side to side in rhythm to the music as a man dressed all in white, his eyes closed and his hands gripping a gold-colored scepter, rocked to and fro in the pulpit. So different, thought Brother Francis, and pagan in a way. Silently, and with a gesture so delicate as to be barely perceptible, he blessed them all: *In Nomine Patris et Filii et Spiritus Sancti amen.* My benediction, he thought (Suffer little children to come unto me). Quite suddenly he was sorry that the Negro in the pink narrow-brimmed hat was not there to receive his blessing with the others. Love thine enemy. The hymn ended more or less at the same time, and there were murmurs of pleasure that died away gradually, and with whispers of delight and satisfaction.

"Gu-lory," said Daddy Happiness.

"Gu-lory," answered his people.

"The worl' is sick with sin an' badness," he went on.

"Sin an' badness."

"The Lord can be an angry Lord."

"An angry Lord."

Brother Francis stayed until the end of the service and then got up before most of the crowd left. He was dimly aware of having passed into another dimension sometime within the past hour and as he descended the stairs, he thought of how impossibly remote were the clawing sounds at the door to his room. He thought too of the mass (smell of incense there, fear in a Gothic chamber), and as he walked down the side street, his mind filled slowly with the memory of the smell, not as he knew it then (or later), but as a boy, when he had sensed the presence of God in the thinning smoke when he and his stepsister had gone to church. The wrathful Giver of Life and Death. He remembered the dust that hovered in the long tapering beams of sunlight (shafts of radiant haze) from the high windows near the ceiling of the church. He had so wanted one of those beams to fall suddenly on his face, to single him from the others and make him known. That was how it was with saints. But what was her name? Her fingers groping between his legs, the drawing feeling of desire that had charged into his loins and bowels (that was there again now as he walked) when she moved the tips of her fingers like quick little insects. He had stayed there while she squeezed gently, rubbing her palm in a tight circular pattern until he seemed forced to return the rhythm, to move against her hand, feeling the swell and throb, the need to go faster each time, to rock against it and help what was to come, to surge. And the third girl on the bench, what was her name? Mary. Her long dark legs that stretched up under the dress. That was where he wanted to be, safe and warm under the dress with the dark thighs against his face (whose painting, the dark cave, warm with moist walls and Saint Francis standing there, his arms outstretched in supplication but) . . . Oh, Jesus, where were those thoughts coming from? What demon?

He walked on quickly now, as if compelled, sensing again the force beyond his reason, remembering that he was guided and instructed, knowing the streets and watching himself move through them as if some third eye of his own were mounted behind him, being both a part of his own perceptions, yet separate from his senses. His feet functioned beneath him (he knew that, he felt them), carrying him forward, but at the precise instant of their setting down and pacing off the sidewalked distance, he saw (and later remembered) them as if he watched from over his own shoulder.

He turned into still another narrow street, this one shimmering with the pulsing glow of neon lights. He passed bar after bar, one on either side of the street, and in the windows —though it was impossible to tell with the glare from the lights—he sensed the leering popeyed faces of those who stood and waited. (Waiting, waiting, we are waiting, we will have you if you come . . .)

Passing by each of the open doors, he smelled the odor of liquor and urine and sawdust, heard the quick staccato blast of trumpets and clarinets, and blinked at the couples who shuffled together on the small dance floors in the rear. The sounds of the music, as he passed the doors to each of the bars, began to merge and flow together in his ears, whistling and pounding a rhythm that seemed (in the mind of that other eye) to be part of a single theme, a taut extended nerve that ran thread-like from instrument to instrument, unaware of walls or distance, having along the way and balancing on its red quivering edge the sounds of birth and death and singing and despair and wailing and joy and grinding metal and crumbling cement: all the sounds of order and chaos that seemed to him a part of that single throbbing wire, one synaptic ending of which adhered to the cells of his brain and the other vanishing in a distant incense-filled chamber, where silks and bells tinkled endlessly from the draperies of gauze that blew in a mountain wind.

The head that held the socket of that other eye turned casually on its mount and watched him pause outside the last of the bars on the street before wiping his hands along the flowered Hawaiian shirt and stepping inside. Then the eye closed quietly (began to wait), and failed to enter with him.

Inside, Brother Francis felt the lumpy sawdust soft and damp beneath his feet (remembered a butcher shop in another time somewhere—the cleaver's *thunk* parting the flesh of a lamb) as he heard the thumping of the drum in the rear, and was suddenly blinded by the tiny amber spotlight

that tapered narrowly from the ceiling behind the bar, and
fell without warning on his face. As he turned and fixed
his eyes directly on the burning filament of the bulb, the
music stopped, then moved into a quicker tempo, a flute
joining the instruments and the drum dropping away to
keep the rhythm beneath the other sounds. The bar was in
darkness except for more tiny spotlights, red and green,
that made shafts of haze through the smoke. And here and
there, with a dull glow burned into his vision, Brother
Francis saw the black faces of the people around him merge
into the darkness, so that in the distance, the bobbing
bodies of the dancers were headless.

"Yes, sir, what will that be?"

It was the bartender, smiling and standing before him,
the same man (but no, that wasn't possible) who had stood
there with the pink narrow-brimmed hat. *You jus' out for
a little walk in the evenin' air?*

"Rye, please. Yes, and with a little beer on the side."

The man walked away down the bar, his feet lifting in
time to the music and his head bobbing in the smoky haze.
He returned the same way, smiling, and Brother Francis
swallowed the rye quickly, then sipped at the beer, almost
at once feeling the brittle edges of the synapse on his brain
loosen and become soft. There . . . that was much better.
He took another long sip from the beer and hardly noticed
the heavy, mauve-dressed woman leave the stool at the end
of the bar and move in his direction. He was humming
softly now, with his eyes half-closed, and moving his head
from side to side. Slowly, then all at once, he reached out
with his mind and embraced the memory of a young girl's
hand between his legs, the touch of resilient thighs at his
fingertips. With the music and smoke around him, being
almost the same quantity and having no line or point at
which one ended and the other began, he savored and enjoyed the thoughts. The girl on the bench, her chocolate
legs reaching up into a warmth of fluff and lace, the white
necks and arms, the slender bodies of the boys he taught.

And the Virgin, she was there again, moving toward him now, without mistake, jeweled bells dangling from her wrists and bare ankles, her thighs showing beneath the pastel gauze, and her hips thrusting at the air from side to side, from front to back, the incensed perfume that flowed from the mist behind her, that came to drug his mind and brought her nearer to him, and nearer still. It was all there for him and he drank again, his eyes still half closed, nodding to the sound of the husky saxophone and the warble of the flute. Yes, he thought, of course. Here and no other place at all. His hips, then his entire body began to move and rotate on the stool—and the sound of a voice beside him made him jump around sharply.

"You got a real swingin' movement there, honey."

It was a Negro woman, heavyset and with her hair dyed a shimmering pink. He stared at her for a moment, the loose flesh hanging from under her arms, the enormous breasts and belly bulging against her mauve-colored dress. He stared without belief, and then the music and smoke again closed in about him and he smiled.

"Man, you don' wanna waste that ol' movement by you'self."

The tinkling swish of bells and silks. The flashing pulse of lights. Without thinking of it, he reached out with his hand, watched it for a moment, then moved it against her soft belly, groping for the feel of her navel with his fingers. He made a muted, high-pitched, pathetic sound in the back of his throat.

"Easy, honey," said the woman. She leaned over and drank the last of his beer, nodded to the bartender, then took him by the hand and led him out over the sawdust floor to the street.

A wind was beginning to stir and bits of dried and brittle paper were blowing noisily across the pavement.

Again he saw himself as from a distance, and felt the wind blowing strongly now against his own (that other person's) face. My wind, he wondered to himself.

"C'mon now, baby," she said.

He slid one hand around under her armpit and placed the other on her breast. A passing couple laughed audibly and pointed at them, but in the world of flesh and hair to come, he hardly heard. There was only the glowing hum of liquor in his ears, but a hum too strong and persistent for the little he had to drink. And through his half-closed and swimming eyes, he could see the Virgin ready to press against him, to wrap her draped arms softly about him, to bring him close against her thighs, flooding him into their warmth.

The breeze hurried, then swept up through the trees, removing forever the memory of the room in Brooklyn, and making a soft howl in the streets that was joined and echoed only by the sobbing laugh in the mouth of Brother Francis.

THE FIELD
NEAR THE
CATHEDRAL
AT CHARTRES

For Mimi Baez

The very first conversation Dick and I had was at Chartres. I was sixteen—it was a strange and beautiful day.

M.F.

The goat cheese, apple brandy, and guitars
had marked our time. People in a painting,
laughing harlequins, we'd strewn our still life
in an old perspective, lounged upon
the mint and sage, and watched an afternoon.
The fields have shores where life might pass us by.
And so it seemed quite right for silences
to grow where breezes shuddered in the orchard,
paused and died. Propped on elbows, giving
ground to city-thought, some failed to praise
the leaving of the day.

Yet even in the morning, strolling
in the gloom of Gothic chambers,
stunned beneath the solemn arch
of artifact and stone, your dance
began. A quick uncertain inching
to your hand, the bangled fingers
searching in the air. We heard
a whispered chorus: voices sounding
all the names of God, easy
echoes, weightless murmurs dabbing
at the walls. Rows of flame
had bowed the pious wax, shaped
the soft and drooping creatures, swayed
a gently melting limb. You bent
an arm and strayed among
the stained reflections, rhythm
of the whispers in your stride.

(Who is that man with calipers,
who creeps and scuttles on a marble floor,
who dreams to know the measure of your step

and fails, bewildered, finding no beginning
nor an end?)

And now as breezes shudder in the orchard,
thick with rhyme and loosed of somber reason—
thought and motion raise their head as one.
Your sudden dance is free of all design.
Young girl, you chose the amber coil of wish,
unlocked it with the cocking of a heel
and stepped away. While in the lunge of flight
I know the tale in your dark body's book.

REFLECTIONS
IN A
CRYSTAL WIND

"Reflections" is the last song we worked on together. I had a dream a few days after he died, that we met and I wanted to hug him and he said, "You can't." He said, "Just embrace me with your thought." And I did, and he answered, and we smiled. And it happens sort of like that from time to time still.

M.F.

If there's a way to say I'm sorry, perhaps I'll stay
    another evening beside your door,
And watch the moon rise inside your window where
    jewels are falling, and flowers weeping, and strangers
    laughing, because you're dreaming that I have gone.

And if I don't know why I'm going, perhaps I'll wait
    beside the pathway where no one's coming,
And count the questions I turned away from,
    or closed my eyes to, or had no time for, or passed right
    over, because the answers would shame my pride.

I've heard them say the word forever, but I don't know
    if words have meaning, when they are promised, in fear
    of losing what can't be borrowed, or lent in blindness,
    or blessed by pageantry, or sold by preachers,
    while you're still walking your separate way.

Sometimes we bind ourselves together, and seldom know
    the harm in binding, the only feeling, that cries for
    freedom and needs unfolding, and understanding,
    and time for holding, a simple mirror
    with one reflection to call your own.

If there's an end to all our dreaming, perhaps I'll go
    while you're still standing beside your door,
And I'll remember your hands encircling, a bowl of
    moonstones, a lamp of childhood, a robe of roses,
    because your sorrows were still unborn.

ABOUT THE AUTHOR

RICHARD FARIÑA, poet, novelist, composer, folk-singer, was born of a Cuban father and an Irish mother, and lived with them, at various times, in Brooklyn, Cuba, and Northern Ireland. At eighteen he became associated with the Irish Republican Army, an experience on which he based his story "An End to a Young Man." He also visited Cuba several times, first while Fidel Castro was still in the mountains, and later when the revolutionary army was entering Havana. He attended Cornell University, leaving in 1959 to live in London and Paris. It was in Paris that work on his widely acclaimed first novel, *Been Down So Long It Looks Like Up to Me,* was begun, some four hours, as Fariña described it, "after I'd finished work as a blind harmonica player."

It was also in France that Richard Fariña met Mimi Baez; in 1963 they were married and returned to California to live. The couple won stunning notices for their performances at the Newport Folk Festival, and their two Vanguard albums "Celebration for a Gray Day" and "Reflections in a Crystal Wind" were also spectacularly successful, the former being selected by *The New York Times* as one of the ten best folk records of 1965.

Two days after the publication of *Been Down So Long It Looks Like Up to Me,* Richard Fariña was killed in a motorcycle accident near Carmel, California.